δ Delta

Focus: Division

Student Text

By Miriam Homer

Math·U·See®

1·888·854·MATH(6284) - MathUSee.com
Sales@MathUSee.com

Math·U·See®

Sales@MathUSee.com - 1·888·854·MATH(6284) - MathUSee.com

Copyright © 2009 by Math·U·See

Graphic Design by Christine Minnich

Printed in the United States of America

Delta

	LESSON PRACTICE			SYSTEMATIC REVIEW			TEST
	A	B	C	D	E	F	
1 Rectangle							
2 Divide ÷ 1, ÷ 2							
3 Divide ÷ 10							
4 Divide ÷ 5, ÷ 3							
5 Parallel, Perpendicular							
6 Divide ÷ 9							
Unit Test 1							
7 Area Parallelogram							
8 Divide ÷ 6							
9 Area Triangle							
10 Divide ÷ 4							
11 Average							
12 Divide ÷ 7, ÷ 8							
Unit Test 2							
13 Area Trapezoid							
14 Thousand, Million							
15 Billion, Trillion							
16 Divide with Remainder							
17 Multiply Up/Down							
18 Divide 2 Digit							
19 Divide 3 Digit							
20 Divide 3 Digit							
21 Round & Estimate							
Unit Test 3							
22 Divide 3 by 2 Digit							
23 Divide 4 by 1 Digit							
24 Divide 4 by 2 Digit							
25 Divide Mult. Digit							
26 Volume							
27 Fraction of Number							
28 Roman Numeral I							
29 Fraction of One							
30 Roman Numeral II							
Unit Test 4							
Final Test							

 QUICK REVIEW

A multiplication problem may be written as 3 x 4, 3 · 4, or (3)(4).

Fill in the parentheses with the factors and write the product in the oval.
Then write the problem two ways beside the rectangle. The first one is done.

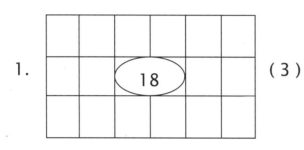

1.   (3)

     18

(6)

6 x 3 = 18

3 x 6 = 18

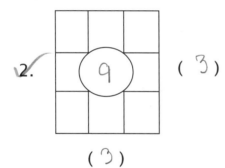

2.   (3)

     9

(3)

3 x 3 = 9

If the figure is a square,
write the problem only
one time.

3.   (2)

     12

(6)

6 · 2 = 12

2 · 6 = 12

4.   (3)

     12

(4)

(3)(4) = 12

(4)(3) = 12

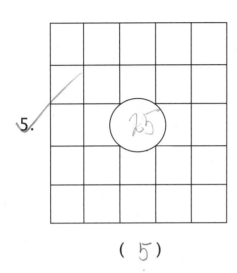

5. (5) $\underline{5} \times \underline{5} = \underline{25}$

(5)

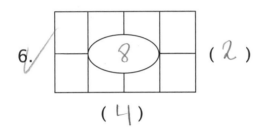

6. (2)

(4)

(2)(4) = $\underline{8}$

(4)(2) = $\underline{8}$

Solve for the unknown. Write your answer above the letter.

7.   6
   6X = 36

8.   10
   2Y = 20

9.   7
   4R = 28

10.   4
   5W = 20

11.   3
   7H = 21

12.   3
   8B = 24

13.   7
   7X = 49

14.   6
   5G = 30

Fill in the parentheses with the factors, and write the product in the oval. Then write the problem beside the rectangle. (Remember that a square is a special kind of rectangle.)

1. 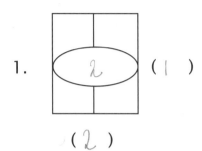 (1) $2 \cdot 1 = 2$

(2)

2. 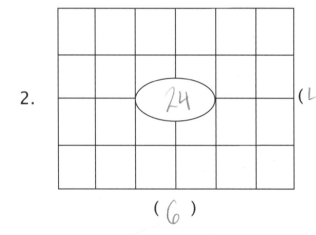 (4) $6 \times 4 = 24$
$4 \times 6 = 24$

(6)

3. 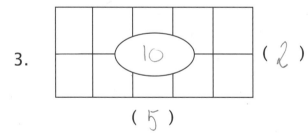 (2) $(2)(5) = 10$
$(5)(2) = 10$

(5)

4. 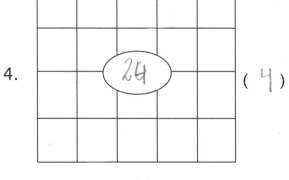 (4) $4 \cdot 5 = 24$
$5 \cdot 4 = 24$

(5)

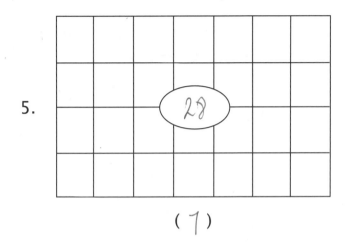

5. (4) $4 \times 7 = 28$

      $7 \times 4 = 28$

      (7)

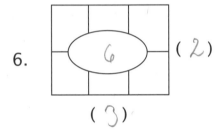

6. (2)

      (3) $(3)(2) = 6$

      $(2)(3) = 6$

Solve for the unknown.

7. $3\overset{1}{X} = 3$

8. $2\overset{2}{Y} = 4$

9. $1\overset{10}{R} = 10$

10. $8\overset{2}{W} = 16$

11. $7\overset{2}{H} = 14$

12. $5\overset{6}{B} = 30$

13. $10\overset{10}{X} = 100$

14. $5\overset{9}{G} = 45$

Fill in the parentheses with the factors, and write the product in the oval. Then write the problem beside the rectangle.

1. 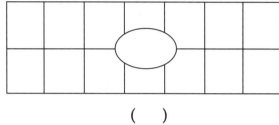 ( )

_____ · _____ = _____

_____ · _____ = _____

2. 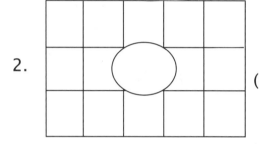 ( )

_____ x _____ = _____

_____ x _____ = _____

3. 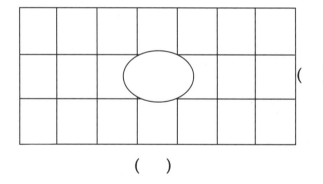 ( )

( )( ) = _____

( )( ) = _____

4. 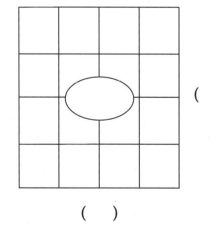 ( )

_____ · _____ = _____

5.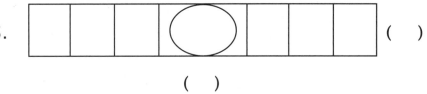

( )

_____ x _____ = _____

_____ x _____ = _____

6. 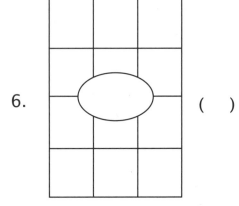 ( )

( ) ( ) = _____

( ) ( ) = _____

( )

Solve for the unknown.

7. 8X = 56   8. 9Y = 36

9. 6R = 24   10. 3W = 27

11. 5H = 45   12. 6B = 18

13. 10X = 90   14. 2G = 16

Fill in the parentheses with the factors, and write the product in the oval.
Then write the problem beside the rectangle.

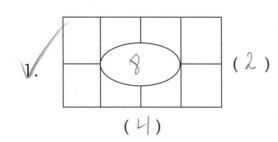

1. (2)

(4)

(2)(4) = 8

(4)(2) = 8

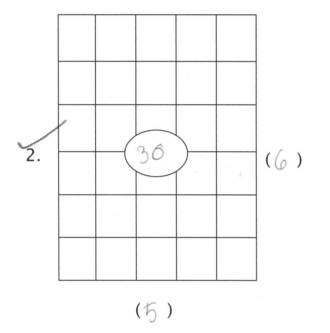

2. (6)

(5)

6 × 5 = 30

5 × 6 = 30

Solve for the unknown.

3. 7A = 49   *7*

4. 10C = 80   *8*

5. 3F = 24   *8*

6. 4B = 36   *9*

QUICK REVIEW

The product of two factors is also the *area* of the rectangle or square. These problems are usually labeled with feet, inches, or some other unit of measure. The product or area should be labeled square inches, square feet, etc.

EXAMPLE 1

3 ft

4 ft

EXAMPLE 2

5"

5"

Area = 3 x 4 = 12 sq ft
(square feet)

Area = 5 x 5 = 25 sq in
(square inches)

Notice that 2 in and 2" both represent two inches, and 2 ft and 2' both stand for two feet. The diagrams may not always be drawn to scale.

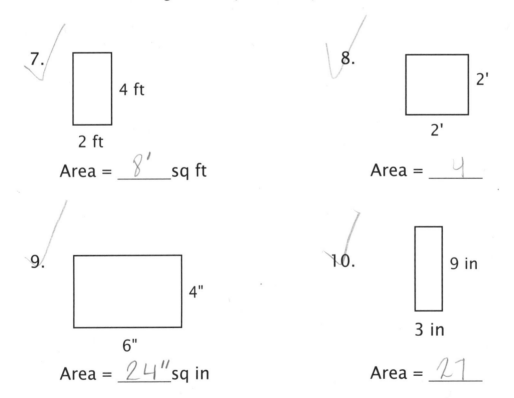

7.

4 ft

2 ft

Area = ___8'___ sq ft

8.

2'

2'

Area = ___4___

9.

4"

6"

Area = ___24"___ sq in

10.

9 in

3 in

Area = ___27___

Fill in the parentheses with the factors, and write the product in the oval. Then write the problem beside the rectangle.

1. 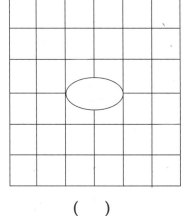   ( )   ____ · ____ = 36

( )

2. 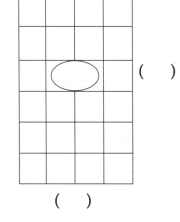   ( )

( )

(   )(   ) = ___

(   )(   ) = ___

Solve for the unknown.

3. 9A = 81

4. 3C = 15

5. 7F = 42

6. 2B = 10

Find the area.

7. 10 mi (miles)

10 mi

Area = _____

8. 4"

8"

Area = _____

9.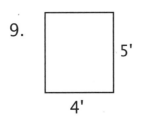

5'

4'

Area = _____

When solving for the unknown, you may use any letter you like. It is helpful to use one that reminds you of the unknown number, like F for flowers in #10.

10. Jenny had 20 flowers and four vases. How many flowers can she put in each vase? (This is solving for the unknown. 4F = 20 flowers) _____

11. Julia owns 30 rabbits. If she can put three rabbits in a hutch, how many hutches does she need? (solving for the unknown) _____

12. A table top is three feet long and two feet wide. What is the area of the table top? _____

Fill in the parentheses with the factors, and write the product in the oval. Then write the problem beside the rectangle.

1. 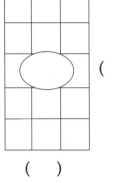 (   )

_____ x _____ = _____

_____ x _____ = _____

(   )

2. (   )

_____ · _____ = _____

_____ · _____ = _____

(   )

Solve for the unknown.

3. 5A = 25

4. 7C = 56

5. 9F = 54

6. 3B = 18

Find the area.

7.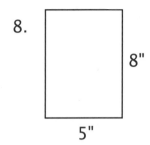
6 ft

6 ft

8.
8"

5"

9.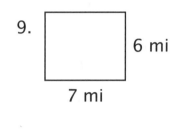
6 mi

7 mi

Area = _____

Area = _____

Area = _____

10. Justina has $24 to spend on gifts for four friends. How much can she spend on each person, if she spends the same amount on each one? _____

11. A job will take 36 hours to complete. If nine people are available to do the job, how many hours must each person work? _____

12. The new park is a rectangle six miles long and five miles wide. What is the area of the park? _____

Answer the questions.

1. How many twos can you count out of eight? __4__

2. How many ones can you count out of ten? __10__

3. How many twos can you count out of fourteen? __7__

4. How many twos can you count out of six? __3__

5. How many ones can you count out of seven? __7__

Divide.

6. $16 \div 2 =$ __8__

7. $9 \div 1 =$ __9__

8. $4 \div 2 =$ __2__

9. $5 \div 1 =$ __5__

10. $18 \div 2 =$ __9__

11. $8 \div 1 =$ __8__

12. $12 \div 2 =$ __6__

13. $2 \div 1 =$ __2__

14. $4 \div 1 =$ __4__

15. $\dfrac{10}{2} =$ __5__

16. $\dfrac{2}{2} =$ __1__

17. $\dfrac{6}{1} =$ __6__

18. $\dfrac{1}{1} =$ __1__

19. $\dfrac{14}{2} =$ __7__

20. $\dfrac{8}{2} =$ __4__

21. Sixteen eyes stared at the teacher. How many people were looking at her? __8__

22. There are 10 cookies and 2 children. How many cookies may each child have? __5__

Answer the questions.

1. How many twos can you count out of ten? __5__

2. How many twos can you count out of sixteen? __8__

3. How many ones can you count out of one? __1__

4. How many ones can you count out of five? __5__

5. How many twos can you count out of twelve? __6__

Divide.

6. $10 \div 2 =$ __5__

7. $16 \div 2 =$ __8__

8. $14 \div 2 =$ __7__

9. $2 \div 2 =$ __1__

10. $2 \div 1 =$ __2__

11. $18 \div 2 =$ __9__

12. $9 \div 1 =$ __9__

13. $8 \div 2 =$ __4__

14. $6 \div 1 =$ __6__

15. $\dfrac{4}{1} =$ __4__

16. $\dfrac{8}{1} =$ __8__

17. $\dfrac{4}{2} =$ __2__

18. $\dfrac{7}{1} =$ __7__

19. $\dfrac{6}{2} =$ __3__

20. $\dfrac{14}{2} =$ __7__

21. There are eight donuts. If each person is to get one donut, how many people can be served? __8__

22. If it is decided to give each person two donuts, how many may be served with eight donuts? __4__

Answer the questions.

1. How many ones can you count out of nine? __9__

2. How many twos can you count out of eighteen? __9__

3. How many ones can you count out of four? __4__

4. How many twos can you count out of twenty? __10__

5. How many twos can you count out of four? __2__

Divide.

6. $2 \div 2 =$ __1__

7. $8 \div 2 =$ __4__

8. $6 \div 2 =$ __3__

9. $4 \div 2 =$ __2__

10. $6 \div 1 =$ __6__

11. $12 \div 2 =$ __6__

12. $10 \div 1 = \underline{10}$

13. $16 \div 2 = \underline{8}$

14. $7 \div 1 = \underline{7}$

15. $\dfrac{14}{2} = \underline{7}$

16. $\dfrac{1}{1} = \underline{1}$

17. $\dfrac{18}{2} = \underline{9}$

18. $\dfrac{9}{1} = \underline{9}$

19. $\dfrac{20}{2} = \underline{10}$

20. $\dfrac{10}{2} = \underline{5}$

21. Twelve ears listened carefully to the speaker. How many people were listening? $\underline{6}$

22. There are six chairs in the room. If only one person sits in each chair, how many people can be seated? $\underline{6}$

2D

Divide.

1. $4 \div 2 =$ ___2___   2. $8 \div 1 =$ ___8___   3. $4 \div 1 =$ ___4___

4. $18 \div 2 =$ ___9___   5. $2 \div 2 =$ ___1___   6. $2 \div 1 =$ ___2___

7. $\dfrac{14}{2} =$ ___7___   8. $\dfrac{16}{2} =$ ___8___   9. $\dfrac{5}{1} =$ ___5___

QUICK REVIEW

There are several ways to write a multiplication problem. Study the following examples. In this lesson, we will be reviewing the five and ten times tables.

EXAMPLE $5 \cdot 4 = 20$ $(5)(4) = 20$ $5 \times 4 = 20$

$$\begin{array}{r} 4 \\ \times\ 5 \\ \hline 2\ 0 \end{array}$$

Multiply.

10. $\begin{array}{r} 5 \\ \times\ 6 \\ \hline 30 \end{array}$

11. $\begin{array}{r} 1\ 0 \\ \times\ 9 \\ \hline 90 \end{array}$

12. $10 \times 6 =$ ___60___

13. $(5)(7) =$ ___35___

Solve for the unknown.

14. 5X = 35
(handwritten: 7)

15. 5R = 45
(handwritten: 9)

16. 10B = 10
(handwritten: 1)

17. 10Y = 40
(handwritten: 4)

Find the area. Label your answers correctly.

18.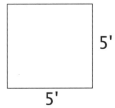

A = 10

19.

A = 15

20.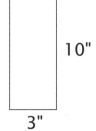

A = 30

21. How many twos can you count out of eighteen? _9_

22. Sally has 18 pennies. If she divides them into piles of two pennies each, how many piles will she have? _9_

Divide.

1. $6 \div 1 =$ _____   2. $8 \div 2 =$ _____

3. $9 \div 1 =$ _____   4. $18 \div 2 =$ _____

5. $2 \div 2 =$ _____   6. $2 \div 1 =$ _____

7. $\dfrac{12}{1} =$ _____   8. $\dfrac{10}{2} =$ _____

9. $\dfrac{1}{1} =$ _____

Solve for the unknown.

10. $5X = 5$ 11. $8R = 80$

12. $7B = 35$ 13. $3Y = 30$

Multiply.

14.   8
    x 5

15.   1 0
   x 7

16. 2 x 10 =_____

17. 10 · 10 =_____

Find the area. Label your answer correctly.

18. 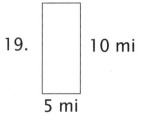 2'

2'

A = _____

19. 10 mi

5 mi

A = _____

20. 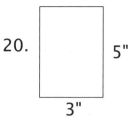 5"

3"

A = _____

21. How many ones can you count out of eight? _____

22. Two birds can live together in a cage. If there are 20 birds, how many cages are needed? _____

Divide.

1. $5 \div 1 =$ _____

2. $16 \div 2 =$ _____

3. $4 \div 2 =$ _____

4. $8 \div 1 =$ _____

5. $14 \div 2 =$ _____

6. $12 \div 2 =$ _____

7. $\frac{18}{2} =$ _____

8. $\frac{10}{2} =$ _____

9. $\frac{20}{2} =$ _____

Solve for the unknown.

10. $5X = 20$

11. $5R = 50$

12. $9B = 90$

13. $5Y = 40$

Multiply.

14.   9
     x 5
     ———

15.   1 0
      x 4
      ———

16. 2 · 5 =____

17. (10)(8) =____

Find the area. Label your answer correctly.

18.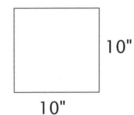

A = _____

19.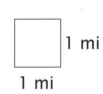

A = _____

20.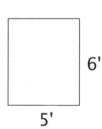

A = _____

21. How many twos can you count out of two? _____

22. Jill has 14 stickers. If she divides them between two friends, how many stickers will each friend receive? _____

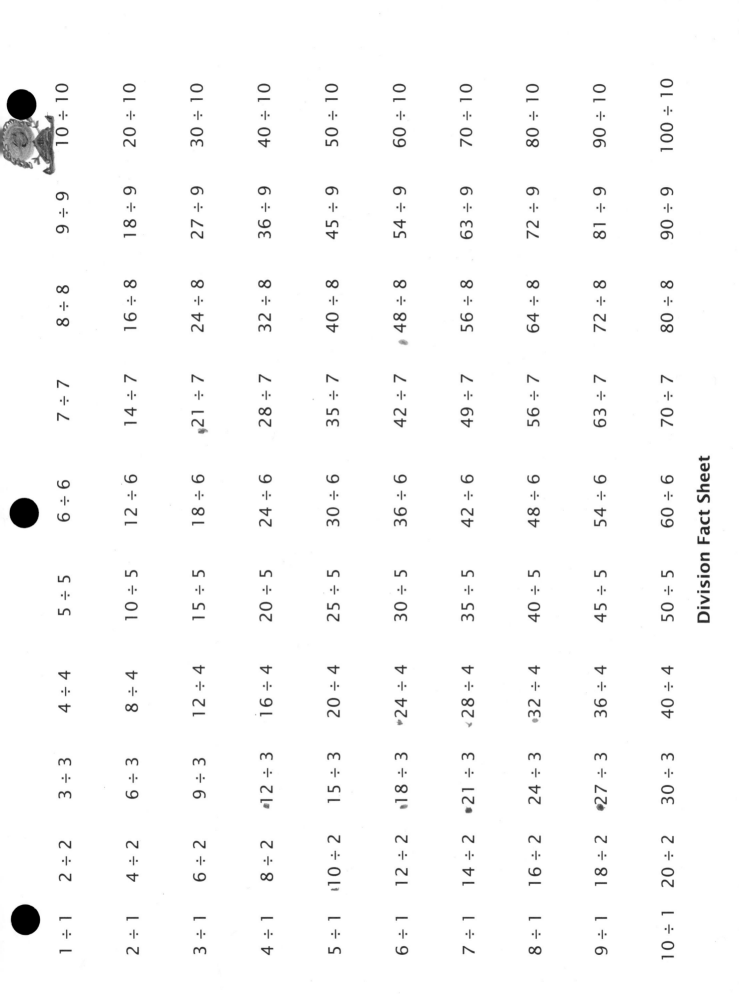

Division Fact Sheet

$1 \div 1$	$2 \div 2$	$3 \div 3$	$4 \div 4$	$5 \div 5$	$6 \div 6$	$7 \div 7$	$8 \div 8$	$9 \div 9$	$10 \div 10$
$2 \div 1$	$4 \div 2$	$6 \div 3$	$8 \div 4$	$10 \div 5$	$12 \div 6$	$14 \div 7$	$16 \div 8$	$18 \div 9$	$20 \div 10$
$3 \div 1$	$6 \div 2$	$9 \div 3$	$12 \div 4$	$15 \div 5$	$18 \div 6$	$21 \div 7$	$24 \div 8$	$27 \div 9$	$30 \div 10$
$4 \div 1$	$8 \div 2$	$12 \div 3$	$16 \div 4$	$20 \div 5$	$24 \div 6$	$28 \div 7$	$32 \div 8$	$36 \div 9$	$40 \div 10$
$5 \div 1$	$10 \div 2$	$15 \div 3$	$20 \div 4$	$25 \div 5$	$30 \div 6$	$35 \div 7$	$40 \div 8$	$45 \div 9$	$50 \div 10$
$6 \div 1$	$12 \div 2$	$18 \div 3$	$24 \div 4$	$30 \div 5$	$36 \div 6$	$42 \div 7$	$48 \div 8$	$54 \div 9$	$60 \div 10$
$7 \div 1$	$14 \div 2$	$21 \div 3$	$28 \div 4$	$35 \div 5$	$42 \div 6$	$49 \div 7$	$56 \div 8$	$63 \div 9$	$70 \div 10$
$8 \div 1$	$16 \div 2$	$24 \div 3$	$32 \div 4$	$40 \div 5$	$48 \div 6$	$56 \div 7$	$64 \div 8$	$72 \div 9$	$80 \div 10$
$9 \div 1$	$18 \div 2$	$27 \div 3$	$36 \div 4$	$45 \div 5$	$54 \div 6$	$63 \div 7$	$72 \div 8$	$81 \div 9$	$90 \div 10$
$10 \div 1$	$20 \div 2$	$30 \div 3$	$40 \div 4$	$50 \div 5$	$60 \div 6$	$70 \div 7$	$80 \div 8$	$90 \div 9$	$100 \div 10$

Answer the questions.

1. How many tens can you count out of eighty? __8__ ✓

2. How many tens can you count out of one hundred? __10__ ✓

3. How many tens can you count out of sixty? __6__ ✓

4. How many tens can you count out of ten? __1__ ✓

Divide.

5. $10\overline{)50}$ = 5 ✓

6. $10\overline{)100}$ = 10 ✓

7. $10\overline{)30}$ = 3 ✓

8. $10\overline{)90}$ = 9 ✓

9. $10\overline{)20}$ = 2 ✓

10. $10\overline{)40}$ = 4 ✓

11. $10 \div 10 =$ __1__ ✓

12. $70 \div 10 =$ __7__ ✓

13. $50 \div 10 =$ __5__ ✓

14. $\dfrac{30}{10} =$ __3__ ✓

15. $\dfrac{90}{10} =$ __9__ ✓

16. $\dfrac{60}{10} =$ __6__ ✓

17. If 10 players are needed for each team, how many teams can be made with 80 players? __8__ ✓

18. How many $10 books can Mrs. Beane buy with $40? __4__ ✓

3B

Answer the questions.

1. How many tens can you count out of twenty? _____

2. How many tens can you count out of forty? _____

3. How many tens can you count out of ninety? _____

4. How many tens can you count out of thirty? _____

Divide.

5. $10\overline{)60}$

6. $10\overline{)90}$

7. $10\overline{)50}$

8. $10\overline{)30}$

9. $10\overline{)70}$

10. $10\overline{)10}$

11. $40 \div 10 =$ _____

12. $20 \div 10 =$ _____

13. $90 \div 10 =$ _____

14. $\dfrac{100}{10} =$ _____

15. $\dfrac{50}{10} =$ _____

16. $\dfrac{10}{10} =$ _____

17. Seventy jelly beans are divided so that each person gets the same amount. If there are 10 people, how many jelly beans does each one receive? _____

18. Shawn can draw 10 pictures on one sheet of paper. How many sheets does he need to draw 30 pictures? _____

3C

Answer the questions.

1. How many tens can you count out of fifty? _____

2. How many tens can you count out of seventy? _____

3. How many tens can you count out of one hundred? _____

4. How many tens can you count out of sixty? _____

Divide.

5. $10 \overline{\smash{\big)}\, 9\,0}$

6. $10 \overline{\smash{\big)}\, 4\,0}$

7. $10 \overline{\smash{\big)}\, 1\,0\,0}$

8. $10 \overline{\smash{\big)}\, 5\,0}$

9. $10 \overline{\smash{\big)}\, 8\,0}$

10. $10 \overline{\smash{\big)}\, 6\,0}$

11. $20 \div 10 =$ _____

12. $30 \div 10 =$ _____

13. $10 \div 10 =$ _____

14. $\dfrac{70}{10} =$ _____

15. $\dfrac{40}{10} =$ _____

16. $\dfrac{30}{10} =$ _____

17. Michael earns 10 dollars an hour. How many hours must he work to earn $50? _____

18. Gabriel got out 100 pennies and divided them into 10 equal piles. How many pennies were in each pile? _____

3D

Divide.

1. $10\overline{)10}$ 1 ✓

2. $10\overline{)30}$ 3 ✓

3. $10\overline{)60}$ 6 ✓

4. $10\overline{)70}$ 7 ✓

5. $1\overline{)5}$ 5 ✓

6. $2\overline{)14}$ 7 ✓

7. $10\overline{)100}$ 10 ✓

8. $1\overline{)10}$ 10 ✓

9. $18 \div 2 = \underline{9}$ ✓

10. $8 \div 1 = \underline{8}$ ✓

11. $\dfrac{50}{10} = \underline{5}$ ✓

12. $\dfrac{16}{2} = \underline{8}$ ✓

Multiply. This lesson will review the three times table.

13. $\begin{array}{r} 9 \\ \times 3 \\ \hline 30 \end{array}$ ✗

14. $\begin{array}{r} 3 \\ \times 4 \\ \hline 12 \end{array}$ ✓

15. $3 \times 7 = \underline{21}$ ✓

16. $10 \cdot 3 = \underline{30}$ ✓

QUICK REVIEW

There are two pints in a quart. Look on your pantry shelf or in your refrigerator if you are not sure how big a pint or a quart is.

Three feet equals one yard. Compare a foot ruler to a yardstick to check for yourself.

Use this information to answer word problems like the following.

Example 1
The store sells honey in cute pint jars. If Sally buys six jars, how any quarts of honey does she have?

$6 \div 2 = 3$ quarts

Example 2
A path is nine yards long. How many feet long is the path?

$3 \times 9 = 27$ feet

17. Ian needs 12 pints of oil for his engine. How many quarts of oil should he buy? __6__

18. Jamie bought eight yards of rope for a project. How many feet of rope does he have? __24__

19. If a piece of paper is five inches wide and eight inches long, what is its area? __40__

20. Alisa bought 12 cans of soda for her two daughters' lunches. How many cans will each girl get? __6__

Divide.

1. $10\overline{)20}$

2. $10\overline{)40}$

3. $10\overline{)90}$

4. $10\overline{)80}$

5. $1\overline{)7}$

6. $2\overline{)20}$

7. $10\overline{)10}$

8. $1\overline{)6}$

9. $8 \div 2 = \underline{\hspace{1cm}}$

10. $4 \div 1 = \underline{\hspace{1cm}}$

11. $\dfrac{6}{2} = \underline{\hspace{1cm}}$

12. $\dfrac{14}{2} = \underline{\hspace{1cm}}$

Multiply.

13. $\begin{array}{r} 3 \\ \times\,3 \\ \hline \end{array}$

14. $\begin{array}{r} 5 \\ \times\,3 \\ \hline \end{array}$

15. (2)(3) = _____

16. 6 x 3 = _____

17. There are 14 pint jars in my cupboard. How many quarts of applesauce will they hold? _____

18. Sam's living room is five yards long. How many feet long is the room? _____

19. The city is planning to build an airport on a piece of land one mile by two miles in size. How many square miles are available for the airport? _____

20. Eighteen ears were listening to the story. How many people were listening? _____

Divide.

1. $10\overline{)70}$

2. $10\overline{)60}$

3. $10\overline{)50}$

4. $10\overline{)30}$

5. $1\overline{)9}$

6. $2\overline{)16}$

7. $2\overline{)4}$

8. $1\overline{)3}$

9. $10 \div 2 =$ _____

10. $12 \div 2 =$ _____

11. $\dfrac{2}{2} =$ _____

12. $\dfrac{18}{2} =$ _____

Multiply.

13. 4
    × 3

14. 3
    × 8

15. 7 · 3 = ____

16. 3 x 9 = ____

17. Sixteen pints of juice are available for the party. How many quarts is that? _____

18. A room is six yards long and three yards wide. How many square yards of carpet are needed to cover the floor? _____

19. How many feet long is the room in #18? _____

    How many feet wide is it? _____

20. Dan has three packages of cookies with 10 cookies in each package. How many cookies does he have? _____

    If he divides the cookies evenly among 10 people, how many cookies will each person receive? _____

Answer the questions.

1. How many fives can you count out of thirty-five? __7__

2. How many fives can you count out of fifty? __10__

3. How many fives can you count out of five? __1__

4. How many threes can you count out of eighteen? __6__

Divide.

5. $5\overline{)45}$ → 9

6. $5\overline{)20}$ → 4

7. $5\overline{)15}$ → 3

8. $3\overline{)30}$ → 10

9. $3\overline{)12}$ → 4

10. $3\overline{)27}$ → 9

11. $30 \div 5 =$ _6_

12. $10 \div 5 =$ _50_

13. $40 \div 5 =$ _8_

14. $\dfrac{25}{5} =$ _5_

15. $\dfrac{24}{3} =$ _8_

16. $\dfrac{21}{3} =$ _7_

17. Nine pieces of candy must be divided among three people. How many pieces does each person get? _3_

18. Three canaries can share a cage. How many cages are needed for 15 canaries? _5_

Answer the questions.

1. How many fives can you count out of forty? _____

2. How many threes can you count out of three? _____

3. How many fives can you count out of twenty-five? _____

4. How many threes can you count out of twenty-seven? _____

Divide.

5. $5\overline{)5}$

6. $5\overline{)35}$

7. $5\overline{)50}$

8. $3\overline{)6}$

9. $3\overline{)24}$

10. $3\overline{)18}$

11. $20 \div 5 =$ _____   12. $45 \div 5 =$ _____

13. $21 \div 3 =$ _____   14. $\dfrac{15}{3} =$ _____

15. $\dfrac{30}{3} =$ _____   16. $\dfrac{30}{5} =$ _____

17. At the bank, Jane-Alice handed the teller 15 one-dollar bills and asked to have them changed to five-dollar bills. How many five-dollar bills should she receive? _____

18. Hannah bought 21 apples and divided them equally among her three children. How many apples did each of the children get?

_____

Answer the questions.

1. How many threes can you count out of nine? _____

2. How many threes can you count out of twenty-four? _____

3. How many fives can you count out of ten? _____

4. How many fives can you count out of twenty? _____

Divide.

5. 3⟌1 2

6. 3⟌2 7

7. 5⟌4 0

8. 3⟌1 5

9. 5⟌1 5

10. 3⟌3 0

11. $25 \div 5 =$ _____

12. $50 \div 5 =$ _____

13. $18 \div 3 =$ _____

14. $\dfrac{30}{5} =$ _____

15. $\dfrac{21}{3} =$ _____

16. $\dfrac{5}{5} =$ _____

17. Twenty-four feet of rope is cut into three-foot lengths. How many three-foot pieces of rope result? _____

18. The teacher saw 35 fingers waving at her. How many hands were raised? _____

Divide.

1. $3\overline{)6}$ 2

2. $5\overline{)30}$ 6

3. $3\overline{)18}$ 6

4. $5\overline{)45}$ 9

5. $3\overline{)15}$ 5

6. $5\overline{)25}$ 5

7. $10\overline{)40}$ 4

8. $2\overline{)16}$ 9

9. $24 \div 3 = \underline{8}$

10. $30 \div 3 = \underline{10}$

11. $\dfrac{14}{2} = \underline{7}$

12. $\dfrac{40}{5} = \underline{8}$

Solve for the unknown.

13. $4X = 12$ 3

14. $6R = 30$ 5

15. $5B = 15$ 3

16. $8Y = 24$ 3

QUICK REVIEW

When adding, if the sum of the units place is more than nine, the extra ten must be regrouped or "carried" to the tens place. Study the following examples.

EXAMPLE 1

$$
\begin{array}{r}
1 \\
3\ 4 \\
+\ 2\ 8 \\
\hline
6\ 2
\end{array}
\quad \rightarrow \quad
\begin{array}{r}
1\ 0 \\
3\ 0 + 4 \\
2\ 0 + 8 \\
\hline
6\ 0 + 2
\end{array}
$$

EXAMPLE 2

$$
\begin{array}{r}
1 \\
4\ 5 \\
3\ 5 \\
\hline
8\ 0
\end{array}
\quad \rightarrow \quad
\begin{array}{r}
1\ 0 \\
4\ 0 + 5 \\
3\ 0 + 5 \\
\hline
8\ 0 + 0
\end{array}
$$

Add. Regroup when necessary.

17.
$$
\begin{array}{r}
2\ 5 \\
+\ 3\ 4 \\
\hline
5\ 9
\end{array}
$$

18.
$$
\begin{array}{r}
7\ 8 \\
+\ 3\ 4 \\
\hline
1\ 1\ 2
\end{array}
$$

19.
$$
\begin{array}{r}
1 \\
4\ 9 \\
+\ 5\ 1 \\
\hline
1\ 0\ 0
\end{array}
$$

20.
$$
\begin{array}{r}
1 \\
6\ 5 \\
+\ 1\ 5 \\
\hline
8\ 0
\end{array}
$$

21. Timothy earned $39 yesterday and $28 today. How much did he earn in all? __67__

$$
\begin{array}{r}
1 \\
3\ 9 \\
+\ 2\ 8 \\
\hline
6\ 7
\end{array}
$$

22. Danny earned $5 a day doing chores. If he has $50, how many days did he do chores? __10__

Divide.

1. $3\overline{)12}$

2. $5\overline{)35}$

3. $5\overline{)15}$

4. $3\overline{)9}$

5. $3\overline{)21}$

6. $2\overline{)10}$

7. $3\overline{)27}$

8. $10\overline{)60}$

9. $8 \div 2 =$ _____

10. $3 \div 1 =$ _____

11. $\dfrac{50}{5}$ = _____

12. $\dfrac{3}{3}$ = _____

Solve for the unknown.

13. $5X = 35$

14. $3R = 21$

15. $7B = 70$

16. $6Y = 18$

Add. Regroup when necessary.

17.
```
  1 3
+ 1 9
```

18.
```
  2 8
+ 4 9
```

19.
```
  2 6
+ 7 2
```

20.
```
  4 7
+ 3 8
```

21. Twenty stickers are divided among five children. How many stickers does each one get? _____

22. If Christie puts three photos on a page, how many pages will she need for 27 photos? _____

23. Ruth made applesauce and filled 10 quart jars and 3 pint jars. How many pints of applesauce did she make? (Be careful: this is a two-step problem.) _____

24. I wrote seven thank-you notes each hour during the first two hours of the day. The next hour I wrote 11 more thank-you notes. How many people did I thank? _____

Divide.

1. $5\overline{)10}$

2. $3\overline{)24}$

3. $3\overline{)30}$

4. $5\overline{)40}$

5. $5\overline{)35}$

6. $5\overline{)15}$

7. $3\overline{)12}$

8. $3\overline{)18}$

9. $18 \div 2 = \underline{\hspace{1cm}}$

10. $70 \div 10 = \underline{\hspace{1cm}}$

11. $\dfrac{27}{3} = \underline{\hspace{1cm}}$

12. $\dfrac{5}{1} = \underline{\hspace{1cm}}$

Solve for the unknown.

13. $5X = 50$

14. $3R = 9$

15. $10B = 90$

16. $9Y = 9$

Add. Regroup when necessary.

17.
```
   8 1
 + 1 8
```

18.
```
   3 7
 + 3 7
```

19.
```
   4 2
 + 2 9
```

20.
```
   7 4
 + 2 5
```

21. Matt read five books a week for nine weeks. How many books did he read? _____

22. Each of Joanne's three children gave her $5 for her birthday. How much money did she receive? _____

Joanne wants to use the money to buy treats for each of the five people in the family. How much can she spend on each person? _____

23. Julie needs pieces of yarn one yard long for a craft project. How many pieces can she cut from 18 feet of yarn? ($18 \div 3$) _____

24. Paul drove 46 miles this morning and 28 miles this afternoon. How many miles did he drive today? _____

5A

For #1–4, look at the drawing, and tell whether the statement is true or false. On these pages, if lines look parallel, assume that they are.

1. Line a is || to line b. _____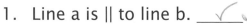

2. Line b is ⊥ to line c. _____

3. Line c is || to line d. _____

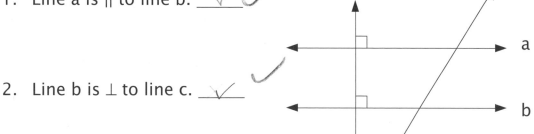

4. Line d is ⊥ to line a. _____ ✗

5. Write the symbol for perpendicular. ⊥

6. Write the symbol for parallel. ||

7. Are the branches of a tree parallel to the trunk? ✗

8. If your house has a slanted roof, is the roof perpendicular to the walls? ✗

9. In dry climates, many homes have flat roofs. Would the roof and walls be perpendicular in those homes? _X_

10. How many sets of parallel sides does a rectangle have? _2_

11. ⊥ stands for _Perpendicular_

12. ‖ stands for _Parallel_ .

For #1–4, look at the drawing, and tell whether the statement is true or false.

1. Line a is || to line d. _____

2. Line a is ⊥ to line d. _____

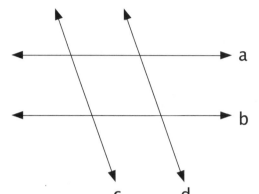

3. Line a is || to line b. _____

4. Line c is || to line d. _____

5. Write the symbol for parallel. _____

6. Write the symbol for perpendicular. _____

7. When building railroad tracks, the workers must first lay cross ties on the gravel before they begin to put down the actual track. The cross ties are _____ to the track.

8. Is it possible to draw a triangle with two parallel sides? _____

9. Can two sides of a triangle be perpendicular to each other? _____

10. A spaceship is launched perpendicular to the earth. If it does not change its course, will it orbit the earth? _____

11. ∥ stands for _____ .

12. ⊥ stands for _____ .

For #1–4, look at the drawing, and tell whether the statement is true or false.

1. Line c is ‖ to line d. _____

2. Line c is ⊥ to line a. _____

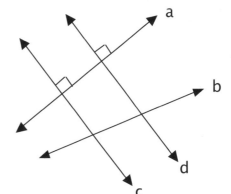

3. Line a is ‖ to line b. _____

4. Line d is ⊥ to line b. _____

5. Write the symbol for perpendicular. _____

6. Write the symbol for parallel. _____

7. David drew a picture of the sun. Do you think the lines representing the sun's rays are parallel to each other? _____

8. Are the spokes on a wheel ever parallel to each other? _____

9. Are the hands of a clock ever perpendicular to each other? _____

10. How many perpendicular corners does a square have? _____

11. ⊥ stands for _____ .

12. || stands for _____ .

Add.

1.
```
   4 5
 + 6 2
 ─────
  10 6
```

2.
```
   1 7
 + 3 4
 ─────
   5 1
```

3.
```
   5 5
 + 5 5
 ─────
  1 1 0
```

4.
```
   2 9
 + 7 1
 ─────
  1 0 0
```

Solve for the unknown to review the nine times table.

5. $9X = 36$ 4

6. $9R = 54$ 8

7. $9B = 81$ 9

8. $9Y = 63$ 7

Divide.

9. $60 \div 10 = \underline{6}$

10. $15 \div 3 = \underline{5}$

11. $\dfrac{14}{2} = \underline{7}$

12. $\dfrac{30}{10} = \underline{3}$

13. 3) 6   *2*

14. 5) 4 5   *9*

15. 2) 1 8   *9*

16. 5) 3 5   *7*

17. Should the walls of your room be perpendicular to the floor? _✓_

18. Are the front and back walls of your house parallel to each other?
_✓_

19. There are five pounds of flour in a bag. How many bags must you buy to get 20 pounds? _4_

20. Peter did 25 math problems in the morning and 38 in the afternoon. How many math problems has he done in all? _53_

5E

Add.

1.
$$\begin{array}{r} 1\ 9 \\ +\ 8\ 8 \\ \hline \end{array}$$

2.
$$\begin{array}{r} 5\ 4 \\ +\ 1\ 3 \\ \hline \end{array}$$

3.
$$\begin{array}{r} 4\ 3 \\ +\ 6\ 7 \\ \hline \end{array}$$

4.
$$\begin{array}{r} 7\ 4 \\ +\ 4\ 8 \\ \hline \end{array}$$

Solve for the unknown to review the nine times table.

5. $9X = 72$

6. $9R = 90$

7. $9B = 18$

8. $9Y = 90$

Divide.

9. $50 \div 10 = \underline{\hspace{1cm}}$

10. $15 \div 5 = \underline{\hspace{1cm}}$

11. $\dfrac{18}{3} = \underline{\hspace{1cm}}$

12. $\dfrac{16}{2} = \underline{\hspace{1cm}}$

13. 10) 3 0   14. 5) 2 5

15. 3) 2 7   16. 2) 1 2

17. The symbol for parallel is _____ .

The symbol for perpendicular is _____ .

18. Is the Leaning Tower of Pisa perpendicular to the ground? _____

19. Justin wants to divide 20 gumdrops between himself and a friend. How many gumdrops will each person get? _____

20. Ruth's garden measures nine feet by nine feet. What is the area of the garden? _____

Add.

1. $\begin{array}{r} 24 \\ +35 \\ \hline \end{array}$

2. $\begin{array}{r} 13 \\ +19 \\ \hline \end{array}$

3. $\begin{array}{r} 81 \\ +79 \\ \hline \end{array}$

4. $\begin{array}{r} 65 \\ +42 \\ \hline \end{array}$

Solve for the unknown to review the nine times table.

5. $9X = 18$

6. $9R = 54$

7. $9B = 72$

8. $9Y = 9$

Divide.

9. $40 \div 5 =$ _____

10. $70 \div 10 =$ _____

11. $\dfrac{21}{3} =$ _____

12. $\dfrac{30}{3} =$ _____

13. $10\overline{)100}$

14. $5\overline{)20}$

15. $3\overline{)24}$

16. $2\overline{)8}$

17. Line a is _____ to line b.

Line c is _____ to line b.

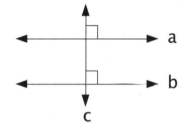

18. If Jim and Joe set out to cross the country on two parallel routes, will they ever meet? _____

19. A vine grew 27 feet last year. How many yards did it grow? _____

20. Sixteen boys and 14 girls went on the picnic. How many children went on the picnic? _____

6A

Answer the questions.

1. How many nines can you count out of thirty-six? __4__

2. How many nines can you count out of twenty-seven? __3__

3. How many nines can you count out of eighteen? __2__

4. How many nines can you count out of fifty-four? __6__

Divide.

5. $9\overline{)81}$ 9

6. $9\overline{)18}$ 2

7. $9\overline{)63}$ 7

8. $9\overline{)45}$ 5

9. $9\overline{)90}$ 10

10. $9\overline{)27}$ 3

11. $9 \div 9 =$ __1__   12. $54 \div 9 =$ __6__

13. $72 \div 9 =$ __8__   14. $\dfrac{36}{9} =$ __6__

15. $\dfrac{81}{9} =$ __9__   16. $\dfrac{45}{9} =$ __5__

17. How much must Pat earn every day in order to earn $90 in nine days? __10$__

18. Thirty-six slices of pizza vanished at the party. There were nine children, and each ate the same number of pieces. How many pieces did each eat? __6__

Answer the questions.

1. How many nines can you count out of forty-five? __5__

2. How many nines can you count out of eighteen? __2__

3. How many nines can you count out of twenty-seven? __3__

4. How many nines can you count out of seventy-two? __8__

Divide.

5. $9\overline{)27}$ 3

6. $9\overline{)54}$ 6

7. $9\overline{)36}$ 4

8. $9\overline{)72}$ 8

9. $9\overline{)45}$ 5

10. $9\overline{)9}$ 1

11. $18 \div 9 =$ _2_

12. $81 \div 9 =$ _9_

13. $63 \div 9 =$ _4_

14. $\dfrac{90}{9} =$ _10_

15. $\dfrac{54}{9} =$ _6_

16. $\dfrac{36}{9} =$ _4_

17. A tower is 81 feet high. If each story is nine feet high, how many stories tall is the tower? _9_

18. Sara needed to bake nine layers for each of the fancy cakes she was making. If the total number of layers she needed was 27, how many cakes was she planning to make? _3_

Answer the questions.

1. How many nines can you count out of ninety? _____

2. How many nines can you count out of eighty-one? _____

3. How many nines can you count out of nine? _____

4. How many nines can you count out of sixty-three? _____

Divide.

5. $9\overline{)54}$

6. $9\overline{)9}$

7. $9\overline{)72}$

8. $9\overline{)45}$

9. $9\overline{)27}$

10. $9\overline{)36}$

11. $18 \div 9 = $ _____

12. $63 \div 9 = $ _____

13. $45 \div 9 = $ _____

14. $\dfrac{72}{9} = $ _____

15. $\dfrac{27}{9} = $ _____

16. $\dfrac{81}{9} = $ _____

17. The twins' combined age was 18. How old was each twin? _____

18. How many baseball teams can be formed with 54 players? (Nine players are on a team.) _____

Divide.

1. $9\overline{)54}$ — 6

2. $9\overline{)45}$ — 5

3. $9\overline{)63}$ — 4

4. $3\overline{)24}$ — 8

5. $5\overline{)35}$ — 7

6. $10\overline{)60}$ — 6

7. $9\overline{)36}$ — 4

8. $2\overline{)18}$ — 9

9. $72 \div 9 = \underline{8}$

10. $90 \div 9 = \underline{10}$

11. $\dfrac{25}{5} = \underline{5}$

12. $\dfrac{21}{3} = \underline{7}$

Solve for the unknown.

13. $5A = 5$ — 1

14. $9Y = 81$ — 9

15. $3R = 12$ — 4

16. $10X = 100$ — 10

QUICK REVIEW

When subtracting, it is sometimes necessary to regroup or "borrow" from the tens place. Study the following example.

EXAMPLE

$$42 \rightarrow 40 + 2 \rightarrow \overset{10}{\overbrace{30 + 2}} \rightarrow 30 + 12$$
$$-18 \quad -(10 + 8) \quad -(10 + 8) \quad -(10 + 8)$$
$$\overline{24} \qquad\qquad\qquad\qquad\qquad \overline{20 + 4}$$

Subtract, regrouping as necessary. The first one is done for you.

17.
$$\begin{array}{r} \overset{2}{\cancel{3}}\,{}^1 4 \\ -1\ 6 \\ \hline 1\ 8 \end{array}$$

18.
$$\begin{array}{r} \overset{6}{\cancel{7}}\,{}^1 4 \\ -3\ 8 \\ \hline 3\ 6 \end{array}$$

19.
$$\begin{array}{r} 5\ 9 \\ -4\ 1 \\ \hline 1\ 8 \end{array}$$

20.
$$\begin{array}{r} 6\ 7 \\ -2\ 5 \\ \hline 4\ 2 \end{array}$$

21. Ida has 81 pine cones that she plans to use to decorate Christmas wreaths. If she uses nine cones for each wreath, how many wreaths can she make? ____9____

22. Brad gave the clerk 95¢ for a comic book that cost 87¢. What was Brad's change? ____8¢____

Divide.

1. $9\overline{)36}$

2. $9\overline{)54}$

3. $9\overline{)18}$

4. $9\overline{)9}$

5. $3\overline{)15}$

6. $5\overline{)20}$

7. $10\overline{)40}$

8. $2\overline{)12}$

9. $27 \div 9 = $ _____

10. $81 \div 9 = $ _____

Solve for the unknown.

11. $\dfrac{72}{9} = $ _____

12. $\dfrac{12}{3} = $ _____

13. $2D = 18$

14. $10X = 50$

Solve for the unknown.

15. 3R = 21

16. 5Y = 45

Add or subtract.

17.   4 3
     - 1 9

18.   7 8
     - 5 9

19.   2 6
     + 7 5

20.   6 7
     - 3 8

21. Terri made 25 pints of apple jelly and 25 pints of grape jelly. If she uses the jelly as gifts for 10 friends, how many pints can she give to each friend? _____

22. Terri made 14 pints of pickles. How many quarts is that? _____

23. The path to the front door is 27 feet long. How many yards of snow must Rick shovel? _____

24. There were 32 ripe oranges on the tree. If we picked 14 of them, how many were left? _____

Divide.

1. $9\overline{)90}$

2. $9\overline{)18}$

3. $9\overline{)36}$

4. $9\overline{)54}$

5. $3\overline{)27}$

6. $5\overline{)40}$

7. $9\overline{)72}$

8. $5\overline{)45}$

9. $80 \div 10 = \underline{\quad}$

10. $16 \div 2 = \underline{\quad}$

Solve for the unknown.

11. $\dfrac{63}{9} = \underline{\quad}$

12. $\dfrac{45}{9} = \underline{\quad}$

Solve for the unknown.

13. $9Z = 72$

14. $3F = 24$

15. $5A = 50$

16. $9B = 0$

Add or subtract.

17.
$$\begin{array}{r} 8\,2 \\ +\,1\,8 \\ \hline \end{array}$$

18.
$$\begin{array}{r} 3\,7 \\ -\,2\,8 \\ \hline \end{array}$$

19.
$$\begin{array}{r} 6\,6 \\ -\,3\,9 \\ \hline \end{array}$$

20.
$$\begin{array}{r} 7\,5 \\ +\,2\,4 \\ \hline \end{array}$$

21. Mom bought eight pints of juice and Dad brought home four pints. How many quarts of juice do we have? _____

22. How many feet are there in nine yards? (Hint: this is a multiplication problem.) _____

23. Forty-five people needed a ride for the field trip. If nine can fit in each van, how many vans are needed? _____

24. Ashley had 28 cents in her purse. She found 35 cents more in her pocket. How many treats can she buy if they cost nine cents apiece? _____

Find the area of the parallelograms. The first one is done for you.

1.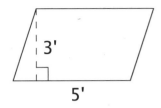

   Area = <u>15 square feet</u>

   (5 x 3 = 15 sq ft)

2.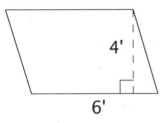

   Area = <u>24 sq.'</u>

3.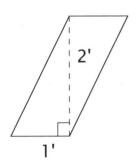

   Area = <u>2 sq.'</u>

4.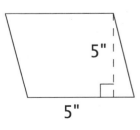

   Area = <u>25</u> square inches

5. 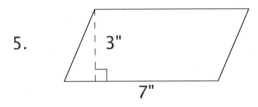   Area = _____ 24 ___ sq in

6. 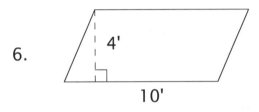   Area = _40 sq. '___

7. George was playing with scissors and paper. He cut a rectangle seven inches long and five inches high. Then he cut a triangle off one end and taped it to the other to make a parallelogram. What was the area of his parallelogram? _35 sq"___

8. Mary was tired of rectangles, so she laid out her new garden in the shape of a parallelogram. If its base was nine yards and its height was five yards, what was the area of her new garden? _45 sq.___

7B

Find the area of the parallelograms.

1. 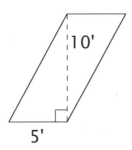   Area = _____

2. 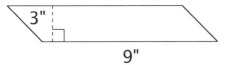   Area = _____

3. 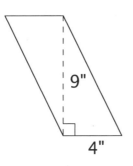   Area = _____

4. 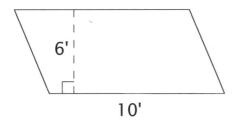   Area = _____

5. 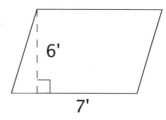   Area = _____

6. 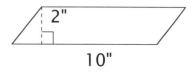   Area = _____

7. The game board is a parallelogram with a base of 10 inches and a height of 10 inches. What is its area? _____

8. Austin cut parallelograms out of adhesive paper to decorate his walls. The shapes are eight inches long and five inches high. How many square inches of paper will he use for each one? _____

Find the area of the parallelograms.

1.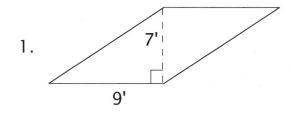

Area = _____

2.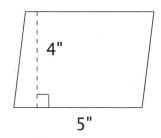

Area = _____

3.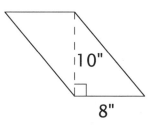

Area = _____

4.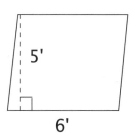

Area = _____

5. 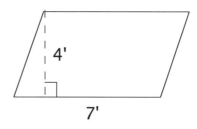   Area = _____

6. 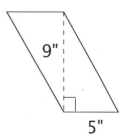   Area = _____

7. The new museum was built with unusual angles. One room forms a parallelogram with a length of eight yards and a distance straight across the floor (height) of nine yards. What is the area of the room? _____

8. The floor of the room next door forms a parallelogram with a base of 10 yards and a height of 9 yards. What is its area? _____

Find the area.

1.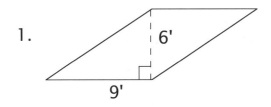

6'

9'

A = ___54 sq.'___

2.

6"

8"

A = ___48 sq."___

3.

10"

5"

A = ___50 sq."___

4.

6 mi

6 mi (miles)

A = ___36 sq. mi___

Divide.

5. $\quad 9 \overline{\smash{\big)}\,36}$ 4

6. $\quad 5 \overline{\smash{\big)}\,45}$ 9

7. $\quad 2 \overline{\smash{\big)}\,18}$ 9

8. $\quad 9 \overline{\smash{\big)}\,63}$ 7

9. $27 \div 3 =$ _8_

10. $35 \div 5 =$ _7_

11. $\dfrac{18}{3} =$ _2_

12. $\dfrac{50}{10} =$ _5_

Solve for the unknown to review the six and four times tables.

13. $6X = 42$ _7_

14. $6R = 30$ _5_

15. $4B = 32$ _8_

16. $6Y = 12$ _2_

Add or subtract.

17.
$$\begin{array}{r} 3\,8 \\ +\,2\,6 \\ \hline 6\,4 \end{array}$$

18.
$$\begin{array}{r} 1\,5 \\ +\,8\,4 \\ \hline 9\,9 \end{array}$$

19.
$$\begin{array}{r} 4\,5 \\ -\,1\,6 \\ \hline 6\,1 \end{array}$$

20.
$$\begin{array}{r} 7\,1 \\ -\,5\,6 \\ \hline 1\,2\,7 \end{array}$$

21. A parallelogram has a base of six inches and a height of five inches. What is its area? _30 sq."_

   A square is four inches on a side. What is its area? _16 sq."_
   Which figure has the largest area? _P_

22. The girls made 43 fancy barrettes. They sold 28 of them. How many are left to sell? _15_

Find the area.

1.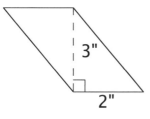

A = _____

2.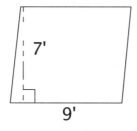

A = _____

3.

A = _____

4.

A = _____

Divide.

5. 3) 1 2

6. 9) 5 4

7. 3) 2 4

8. 5) 2 5

9. $14 \div 2 =$ _____

10. $8 \div 1 =$ _____

11. $\dfrac{81}{9} =$ _____

12. $\dfrac{21}{3} =$ _____

Solve for the unknown to review the six and four times tables.

13. $4X = 24$

14. $6R = 60$

15. $6B = 42$

16. $4Y = 28$

Add or subtract.

17.
$$\begin{array}{r} 7\ 1 \\ +\ 6\ 2 \\ \hline \end{array}$$

18.
$$\begin{array}{r} 4\ 3 \\ -\ 2\ 5 \\ \hline \end{array}$$

19.
$$\begin{array}{r} 9\ 2 \\ +\ 1\ 1 \\ \hline \end{array}$$

20.
$$\begin{array}{r} 5\ 7 \\ +\ 4\ 6 \\ \hline \end{array}$$

21. Joanne took a ride on a train. Were the train tracks parallel or perpendicular to each other? _____

22. The balcony on the new building was shaped like a parallelogram. The floor was five yards long and had a distance straight across of three yards. What was the area of the balcony floor? _____

Find the area.

1.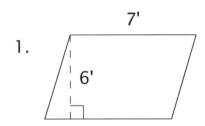

A = _____

2.

A = _____

3.

A = _____

4.

A = _____

Divide.

5. $9 \overline{)27}$

6. $3 \overline{)15}$

7. $5 \overline{)30}$

8. $2 \overline{)16}$

9. $72 \div 9 =$ ____

10. $90 \div 10 =$ ____

11. $\dfrac{20}{2} =$ _____

12. $\dfrac{45}{9} =$ _____

Solve for the unknown to review the six and four times tables.

13. $4X = 32$

14. $6R = 48$

15. $6B = 36$

16. $4Y = 16$

Add or subtract.

17.
$$\begin{array}{r} 2\,1 \\ -\ \ 9 \\ \hline \end{array}$$

18.
$$\begin{array}{r} 7\,6 \\ +\,5\,4 \\ \hline \end{array}$$

19.
$$\begin{array}{r} 3\,3 \\ +\,4\,5 \\ \hline \end{array}$$

20.
$$\begin{array}{r} 6\,4 \\ -\,2\,5 \\ \hline \end{array}$$

21. Frank has 14 pint jars filled with peaches. How many quarts of peaches does he have? _____

22. Tom's mom asked him to read 30 books over vacation. If he has read 16 books so far, how many does he have left to read? _____

Answer the questions.

1. How many sixes can you count out of eighteen? __3__

2. How many sixes can you count out of fifty-four? __9__

3. How many sixes can you count out of twelve? __2__

4. How many sixes can you count out of sixty? __10__

Divide.

5. $6 \overline{)12}$ 2

6. $6 \overline{)6}$ 1

7. $6 \overline{)24}$ 4

8. $6 \overline{)36}$ 6

9. $6 \overline{)42}$ 7

10. $6 \overline{)18}$ 3

11. $60 \div 6 =$ __10__

12. $24 \div 6 =$ __4__

13. $42 \div 6 =$ __7__

14. $\dfrac{54}{6} =$ __9__

15. $\dfrac{30}{6} =$ __5__

16. $\dfrac{48}{6} =$ __8__

17. How many ants are present if there are 24 legs? (Ants have six legs apiece.) __4__

18. How much must Dana earn every day in order to earn \$30 in six days? __5 #__

Answer the questions.

1. How many sixes can you count out of thirty? _5_

2. How many sixes can you count out of six? _1_

3. How many sixes can you count out of twenty-four? _4_

4. How many sixes can you count out of forty-eight? _8_

Divide.

5. $6\overline{)36}$ → 6

6. $6\overline{)60}$ → 10

7. $6\overline{)30}$ → 5

8. $6\overline{)18}$ → 3

9. $6\overline{)54}$ → 9

10. $6\overline{)42}$ → 7

11. $6 \div 6 =$ __1__

12. $24 \div 6 =$ __4__

13. $18 \div 6 =$ __3__

14. $\dfrac{30}{6} =$ __5__

15. $\dfrac{48}{6} =$ __8__

16. $\dfrac{12}{6} =$ __2__

17. If it took Marie six minutes to play a song on her harp, how many songs could she play in one hour? (1 hour = 60 minutes)
__10__

18. Roger earned $54 in six hours. How much did he earn each hour? __9__

Answer the questions.

1. How many sixes can you count out of fifty-four? _____

2. How many sixes can you count out of thirty-six? _____

3. How many sixes can you count out of sixty? _____

4. How many sixes can you count out of forty-two? _____

Divide.

5. $6\overline{)18}$　　　　　　6. $6\overline{)54}$

7. $6\overline{)6}$　　　　　　8. $6\overline{)30}$

9. $6\overline{)12}$　　　　　　10. $6\overline{)24}$

11. $42 \div 6 =$ _____

12. $36 \div 6 =$ _____

13. $48 \div 6 =$ _____

14. $\dfrac{60}{6} =$ _____

15. $\dfrac{54}{6} =$ _____

16. $\dfrac{12}{6} =$ _____

17. Shane has \$48 to spend on Christmas gifts for six of his friends. How much will he be able to spend on each friend? _____

18. A carpenter has a board that is 18 feet long. If he saws it into six equal lengths, how many feet long will each piece be? _____ How many yards long is each piece? _____

Divide.

1. $6\overline{)18}$ 3

2. $6\overline{)42}$ 7

3. $6\overline{)54}$ 9

4. $3\overline{)24}$ 8

5. $5\overline{)25}$ 5

6. $2\overline{)18}$ 9

7. $9\overline{)54}$ 6

8. $10\overline{)60}$ 6

9. $48 \div 6 = \underline{8}$

10. $72 \div 9 = \underline{8}$

11. $\dfrac{21}{3} = \underline{7}$

12. $\dfrac{35}{5} = \underline{7}$

Find the area.

13. 6' , 12'

A = $\underline{2'}$

14. 7", 3"

A = $\underline{21''}$

15. 4", 4"

A = $\underline{1''}$

QUICK REVIEW

Place-value notation can be used to check your work when multiplying. Be sure to place each "carry" in the proper column. Study the example.

EXAMPLE

```
      1 4
   ×  1 7
      ②
  ① 7 8
    1 4
    2 3 8
```

```
      1 0 + 4
   ×  1 0 + 7
        ⓶⓪
 ⑴⓪⓪  7 0 + 8
  1 0 0 + 4 0
  2 0 0 + 3 0 + 8
```

Multiply. Check your work with place-value notation.

16.
```
    2 3
  × 3 6
  1 3 8
 + 6 9 0
  8 2 8
```

17.
```
    7 8
  × 3 4
```

18.
```
    6 5
  × 1 5
```

19. Each of the 12 white mice had 15 babies. How many baby mice is that? _____

20. The area of a rectangle is 45 square feet and the area of a parallelogram is 61 square feet. What is the difference between their areas? _____

21. Sophie bought 36 skeins of yarn. If she uses six skeins for each afghan, how many afghans can she make? _____

22. Kevin earned $39 yesterday and $28 today. How much did he earn in all? _____

Divide.

1. $6\overline{)12}$ **2**

2. $6\overline{)60}$ **10**

3. $6\overline{)42}$ **7**

4. $6\overline{)24}$ **4**

5. $9\overline{)27}$ **3**

6. $5\overline{)40}$ **8**

7. $10\overline{)20}$ **2**

8. $3\overline{)12}$ **4**

9. $15 \div 3 =$ __5__

10. $30 \div 6 =$ __5__

11. $\dfrac{6}{6} =$ __1__

12. $\dfrac{12}{2} =$ __6__

Add or subtract.

13.
$$\begin{array}{r} 1 \\ 1\,3 \\ +\,1\,9 \\ \hline 3\,2 \end{array}$$

14.
$$\begin{array}{r} 1 \\ 2\,8 \\ +\,4\,9 \\ \hline 7\,7 \end{array}$$

15.
$$\begin{array}{r} 6\,12 \\ 7\,2 \\ -\,2\,6 \\ \hline 4\,6 \end{array}$$

16.
$$\begin{array}{r} 3\,17 \\ 4\,7 \\ -\,3\,8 \\ \hline 8\,9 \end{array}$$

Multiply. Check your work with place-value notation.

17. $\begin{array}{r} \overset{1}{4}\,5 \\ \times\,2\,2 \\ \hline 9\,0 \\ 9\,0\,0 \\ \hline 9\,9\,0 \end{array}$

18. $\begin{array}{r} \overset{2}{1}\,6 \\ \times\,1\,4 \\ \hline 6\,4 \\ 1\,6\,0 \\ \hline 2\,2\,4 \end{array}$

19. $\begin{array}{r} \overset{4}{3}\,9 \\ \times\,\;\,5 \\ \hline 1\,9\,5 \end{array}$

20. Don bought 30 feet of cable for a dog run. How many yards long will his dog run be? __10__

   If the cost of the cable is $6 a yard, what is the total cost? __$60__

21. A parallelogram has a base of 14 inches and a height of 18 inches. What is its area? __243__

22. Paul drove 46 miles this morning and 28 miles this afternoon. How many miles did he drive today? __74 m.__

Divide.

1. $6 \overline{)48}$

2. $6 \overline{)18}$

3. $6 \overline{)12}$

4. $6 \overline{)36}$

5. $9 \overline{)72}$

6. $6 \overline{)54}$

7. $3 \overline{)27}$

8. $5 \overline{)45}$

9. $70 \div 10 = \underline{\qquad}$

10. $16 \div 2 = \underline{\qquad}$

11. $\dfrac{42}{6} = \underline{\qquad}$

12. $\dfrac{60}{6} = \underline{\qquad}$

Add or subtract.

13. $\begin{array}{r} 85 \\ +18 \\ \hline \end{array}$

14. $\begin{array}{r} 47 \\ -38 \\ \hline \end{array}$

15. $\begin{array}{r} 49 \\ +21 \\ \hline \end{array}$

16. $\begin{array}{r} 64 \\ -25 \\ \hline \end{array}$

Multiply. Check your work with place value-notation.

17.   3 3
      x 2 4
    ———————

18.   4 4
      x 1 4
    ———————

19.   1 5
      x 1 5
    ———————

20. Twenty-four people are lined up for a ride at the fair. If six people can ride at one time, how many turns will be needed to give everyone a ride? _____

21. Mr. Rich made $35 an hour. If he worked for 14 hours, how much did he earn? _____

22. A parallelogram has an area of 42 square feet. If the height is six feet, what is the length of the base? (divide) _____

Find the area of the triangles. The first one is done for you.

1.
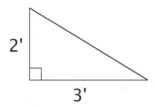

Area = ___3 sq ft___

(2 x 3 = 6 and 6 ÷ 2 = 3)

2.
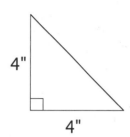

Area = $\dfrac{b \cdot h = 4 \text{sq.}''}{2}$

3.

Area = $\dfrac{b \cdot h = 7 \text{sq.mi}}{2}$

4.
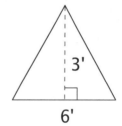

Area = $\dfrac{b \cdot h = 9 \text{sq.}'}{2}$

5.
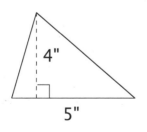

Area = $\dfrac{b \cdot h = 10 \text{sq.}''}{2}$

6.
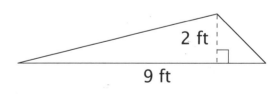

Area = $\dfrac{b \cdot h = 9 \text{sq.}'}{2}$

7.

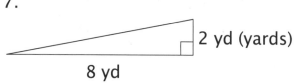

2 yd (yards)

8 yd

8.

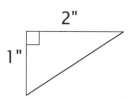

2"

1"

Area = $\underline{b \cdot h}$ = 8 sq. yd
2

Area = $\underline{b \cdot h}$ = 1 sq. "
2

9. What is the area of a triangular plot of land with a base length of two miles and a height of two miles? $\underline{b \cdot h}$ = 8 sq. mi
2

10. Molly cut out a rectangle that measured two inches by four inches. Then she cut the rectangle in half to make two triangles. What is the area of each triangle? $\underline{b \cdot H}$ = 16 sq. "
2

Find the area of the triangles.

1.

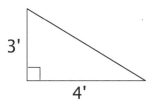

Area = $\dfrac{b \cdot h = 6}{2}$

2.

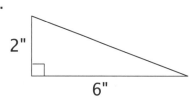

Area = $\dfrac{b \cdot h = 6}{2}$

3.

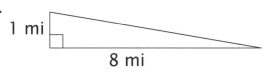

Area = $\dfrac{b \cdot h = 4}{2}$

4.

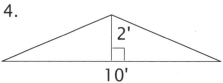

Area = $\dfrac{b \cdot h = 10}{2}$

5.

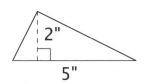

Area = $\dfrac{b \cdot h = 5}{2}$

6.

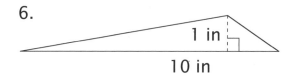

Area = $\dfrac{b \cdot h = 5}{2}$

7.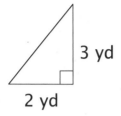

8.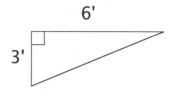

Area = _____   Area = _____

9. Look at the triangle in #8 and change each dimension to yards. What are the base and height of the triangle in yards?

_____ , _____

10. Use your answer to #9 to find the area of the triangle in yards.

_____

Compare this answer with your answer to #8.

Find the area of the triangles.

1.

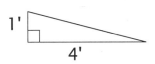

Area = _____

2.

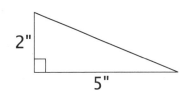

Area = _____

3.

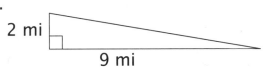

Area = _____

4.

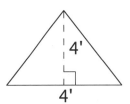

Area = _____

5.

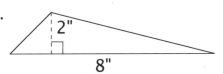

Area = _____

6.

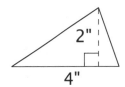

Area = _____

7.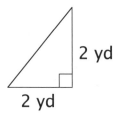

Area = _____

8.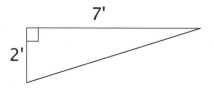

Area = _____

9. Pam laid out a triangular garden with a base of four feet and a height of three feet. The plants she plans to buy will each grow to cover one square foot. How many plants should she buy?

_____

10. Carpet is sometimes sold by the square yard. How many square yards are needed to cover a triangular area with a base of six yards and a height of three yards? _____

Find the area.

1.

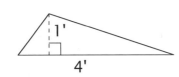

$A = \underline{\dfrac{b \cdot h = 2}{2}}$

2.

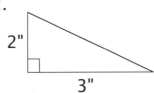

$A = \underline{\dfrac{b \cdot h = 3}{2}}$

3.

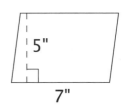

$A = \underline{\dfrac{b \cdot h = 15}{2}}$

Divide.

4. $6 \overline{\smash{)}36}$ 6

5. $6 \overline{\smash{)}42}$ 7

6. $6 \overline{\smash{)}18}$ 3

7. $6 \overline{\smash{)}54}$ 9

8. $63 \div 9 = \underline{7}$

9. $40 \div 5 = \underline{8}$

10. $\dfrac{27}{3} = \underline{9}$

11. $\dfrac{80}{10} = \underline{8}$

Multiply.

12.
```
    5 0
  x 3 2
   1 0 0
  1,530
  1,630
```

13.
```
     4
    1 6
  x 1 8
   1 2 8
   1 6 0
   2 8 8
```

14.
```
    2 8
  x 2 2
      5 6
  5 6 0
  6 1 6
```

15.
```
    3 2
  x 1 7
   2 2 4
   3 2 0
   7 4 4
```

QUICK REVIEW

When adding columns of numbers, it is helpful to look for combinations that make 10. Regroup as you did when adding two numbers. Study the examples.

EXAMPLES

```
        8 ⎞
        2 ⎠ 10
        4 ⎞
      + 6 ⎠ 10
      ─────
      2 0
```

```
      2
      2 5 ⎞
      1 3 ⎠ 10
      1 5 ⎞
    + 3 7 ⎠ 10
    ─────
    9 0
```

```
      1
      1 4 ⎞
      4 6 ⎠ 10
    + 2 4
    ─────
    8 4
```

Add. Make 10 when possible.

16.
```
    2 3
    2 6
  + 3 7
  ─────
```

17.
```
    1 2
    5 9
  + 3 1
  ─────
```

18.
```
    1 5
    1 5
    4 4
  + 2 4
  ─────
```

19.
```
    3 4
    5 6
    1 1
  + 9
  ─────
```

20. A secretary had to type four reports. One report was 5 pages long, one was 11 pages long, one was 4 pages long, and one was 8 pages long. How many pages did she have to type? _____

Find the area.

1.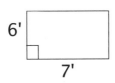

A = _____

2.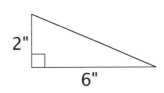

A = _____

3.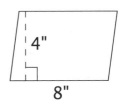

A = _____

Divide.

4. 6 $\overline{)30}$

5. 6 $\overline{)48}$

6. 6 $\overline{)12}$

7. 6 $\overline{)24}$

8. 72 ÷ 9 = _____

9. 27 ÷ 9 = _____

10. $\dfrac{35}{5}$ = _____

11. $\dfrac{3}{3}$ = _____

Subtract.

12.	60 - 3 1	13.	27 - 1 8	14.	5 2 - 2 7

Add. Make 10 when possible.

15.	1 6 7 2 3 8 + 3 1	16.	8 0 1 4 6 8 4 3 + 7 2	17.	5 3 9 8 4 7 1 + 2 6

18. There are 54 people who want to play. How many teams of nine each can be formed? _____

19. Mark bought seven quarts of oil for his truck. How many pints did he buy? _____

20. How many sets of parallel sides does a parallelogram have?
_____

Find the area.

1.

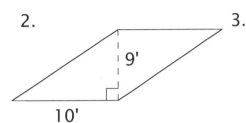

5'

5'

2.

9'

10'

3.

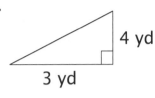

4 yd

3 yd

A = _____   A = _____   A = _____

Divide.

4. 6 | 6 0   5. 9 | 3 6

6. 18 ÷ 3 = ____   7. $\frac{20}{5}$ = ____

Multiply.

8.   4 5   9.   5 2   10.   7 6
    x 1 6   x 2 8   x 5 4

Add. Make 10 when possible.

11.	3 3	12.	8 3	13.	2 6
	7 5		9 0		4 3
	4 4		4 5		3 1
	+ 6 7		2 5		5 7
			+ 1 7		+ 1 4

14. Samuel has $45 dollars. Tickets to the fair cost $5. How many friends can he take along with him? _____

15. Twenty-one toys must be packed into boxes. If three toys fit in a box, how many boxes are needed? _____

16. Gina divided 42 treats among her 6 children. How many treats did each child receive? _____

17. During the game, Jim earned 11 points, Bill earned 9 points, and Tom earned 13 points. How many points did they earn in all?

_____

18. I had 62¢. After I paid my sister 49¢, how much money did I have left over? _____

19. Each box contains 12 cookies. If Martha buys 25 boxes, how many cookies will she have? _____

20. Are any of the touching sides of a stop sign perpendicular? _____

Answer the questions.

1. How many fours can you count out of twenty? __5__

2. How many fours can you count out of eight? __2__

3. How many fours can you count out of twenty-eight? __7__

Divide. Put the product under the number in the box and subtract. The first one is done for you.

4.
```
       6
   4 | 2 4
     -2 4
       0
```

5.
```
      10
   4 | 4 0
     -4 0
       0 0
```

6.
```
       1
   4 | 4
     -4
      0
```

7.
```
       5
   4 | 2 0
     -2 0
       0 0
```

8.
```
       8
   4 | 3 2
     -3 2
       0 0
```

9.
```
       7
   4 | 2 8
     -2 8
       0 0
```

10. $12 \div 4 =$ __3__

11. $36 \div 4 =$ __9__

12. $40 \div 4 =$ _10_   13. $\dfrac{16}{4} =$ _4_

14. $\dfrac{32}{4} =$ _8_   15. $\dfrac{36}{4} =$ _9_

16. The four men on the life raft have 24 cups of water in all. How many cups of water can each man have? _6_

17. Richard has to make 28 Christmas gifts. If he can make four a day, how long will it take? _7 days_

18. A chair has four legs. How many chairs are there if there are 16 legs? _4_

Answer the questions.

1. How many fours can you count out of thirty-six? __9__

2. How many fours can you count out of four? __1__

3. How many fours can you count out of twelve? __3__

Divide. Put the product under the number in the box and subtract.

4. $4\overline{)32}$ 8

5. $4\overline{)16}$ 4

6. $4\overline{)8}$ 2

7. $4\overline{)24}$ 6

8. $4\overline{)12}$ 3

9. $4\overline{)36}$ 9

10. $20 \div 4 =$ ___5___

11. $28 \div 4 =$ ___7___

12. $32 \div 4 =$ ___8___

13. $\dfrac{40}{4} =$ ___10___

14. $\dfrac{4}{4} =$ ___1___

15. $\dfrac{24}{4} =$ ___6___

16. June has 36 fancy stamps used to decorate greeting cards. If she uses four different stamps for each card, how many cards can she make? ___9___

17. Adam earned $4 an hour doing chores. If he earned $20, how many hours did he work? ___5___

18. Forty hooves pounded as the herd galloped across the pasture. How many horses were in the herd? ___10___

Answer the questions.

1. How many fours can you count out of twenty-four? _____

2. How many fours can you count out of sixteen? _____

3. How many fours can you count out of thirty-two? _____

Divide. Put the product under the number in the box and subtract.

4. 4 | 8

5. 4 | 2 8

6. 4 | 4 0

7. 4 | 3 6

8. 4 | 2 0

9. 4 | 4

10. $12 \div 4 =$ _____   11. $24 \div 4 =$ _____

12. $16 \div 4 =$ _____   13. $\dfrac{8}{4} =$ _____

14. $\dfrac{28}{4} =$ _____   15. $\dfrac{40}{4} =$ _____

16. Alice had 32 white mice. How many cages will she need if she keeps four in a cage? _____

17. Four friends looked longingly at the box of chocolates. If there are 28 chocolates, how many will each have? _____

18. The tree in Ben's backyard grows four feet taller each year. How many years will it take the tree to grow eight feet taller? _____

Divide. Continue to write your product under the number in the box.

1. $4\overline{)36}$ 9

2. $4\overline{)20}$ 5

3. $4\overline{)16}$ 4

4. $4\overline{)28}$ 7

5. $36 \div 6 = \underline{6}$

6. $14 \div 2 = \underline{7}$

7. $\dfrac{15}{3} = \underline{5}$

8. $\dfrac{81}{9} = \underline{9}$

Follow the signs.

9.
```
  1 3
  2 5
  3 7
+ 4 2
-----
1 1 7
```

10.
```
  2 11
  3 1
- 2 2
-----
  0 9
```

11.
```
  4 18
  5 8
- 3 9
-----
  1 9
```

12.
```
    4 5
  x 1 5
-------
  2 1 0
+ 4 5 0
-------
1,2 6 0
```

Find the area.

13. 12' 25'

14. 12" 6"

15. 2" 5"

$A = \underline{b \cdot h = 300}$'

$A = \underline{b \cdot h = 72}$"

$A = \underline{\dfrac{b \cdot h}{2}}$

QUICK REVIEW

There are four quarts (qt) in one gallon (gal). Look at a gallon container of juice or milk to visualize a gallon.

Four quarters make one dollar (4 x 25¢ = 100¢ or $1.00).

To change from smaller units to larger units, you divide. To change from larger units to smaller, you multiply. Study the examples carefully.

EXAMPLE 1   Mom needs 16 quarts of milk. How many gallons should she buy?

$$16 \div 4 = 4 \text{ gallons}$$

EXAMPLE 2   Sam has five dollars worth of quarters. How many quarters does he have?

$$4 \times 5 = 20 \text{ quarters}$$

16. Mrs. Smith went to the bank and traded $8 for quarters. How many quarters did she receive? _32_

17. Eight quarts of juice were bought to make punch for the party. How many gallons is that? _32_

18. Mr. Fisher needs six gallons of paint. The store has only quart containers. How many quarts should he purchase? _24_

Divide. Continue to write your product under the number in the box.

1. $4\overline{)40}$

2. $4\overline{)12}$

3. $4\overline{)32}$

4. $4\overline{)24}$

5. $100 \div 10 =$ _____

6. $35 \div 5 =$ _____

7. $\dfrac{27}{9} =$ _____

8. $\dfrac{54}{6} =$ _____

Follow the signs.

9.
```
    4 6
    1 4
    2 3
  + 1 7
  ─────
```

10.
```
    7 6
  - 4 7
  ─────
```

11.
```
    6 4
  x 3 2
  ─────
```

12.
```
    4 3
  x 8 4
  ─────
```

Find the area.

13.   5' 4'

14.  23 mi 28 mi

15. 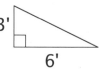 3' 6'

A = _____   A = _____   A = _____

16. Tom paid $28 for four pillows. How much did each pillow cost?

_____

17. Sally has 20 quarters. How many dollars is that? _____

18. Twelve boxes of books arrived in the mail. If there were 24 books in each box, how many books did I receive? _____

19. The Boston Celtics took 45 shots during the first half of the game. If each of the five starters took the same number of shots, how many shots did each one take? _____

20. The corner store sold the following numbers of quarts of orange juice during the last four days: 6, 8, 10, and 12. How many quarts were sold in all? _____

How many gallons of orange juice was that? _____

Divide. Continue to write your product under the number in the box.

1. $4\overline{)16}$

2. $4\overline{)4}$

3. $4\overline{)40}$

4. $4\overline{)8}$

5. $18 \div 2 = \underline{\quad}$

6. $24 \div 3 = \underline{\quad}$

7. $\dfrac{42}{6} = \underline{\quad}$

8. $\dfrac{72}{9} = \underline{\quad}$

Follow the signs.

9.
```
    3 8
    4 1
    1 2
  +   9
```

10.
```
    5 6
    2 4
    1 8
  + 2 1
```

11.
```
    9 1
  - 2 7
```

12.
```
    7 5
  - 2 5
```

Find the area.

13. 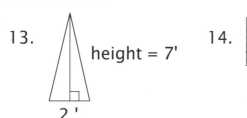 height = 7' 2'

14. 9 mi 16 mi

15. 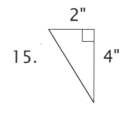 2" 4"

A = _____

A = _____

A = _____

16. Teresa was organizing her office. She needed 12 boxes to store all her supplies. The boxes come in packs of four. How many packs did Teresa buy? _____

17. How many dollars are needed to equal 32 quarters? _____

18. Each side of a square measures 46 feet. What is the area of the square? _____

19. Elliot collects fireflies. He caught 16 on Monday, 19 on Tuesday, 10 on Wednesday, and 15 on Thursday. By Friday morning, how many fireflies were living in his room? _____

    If his mother took two minutes to catch each firefly, how long did she spend catching them all? _____

20. Twenty-four people want to play a game. Four people can be on a team. How many teams can be made? _____

Find the average of the given numbers. The first one is done for you.

1. 2, 7, 9

$2 + 7 + 9 = 18$

$18 \div 3 = 6$

Average = __6__

2. 5, 4, 6

$15 \div 3 = 5$

Average = __5__

3. 8, 8, 5

$21 \div 3 = 7$

Average = __7__

4. 9, 11

$20 \div 2 = 10$

Average = __10__

5. 2, 3, 1

$6 \div 3 = 2$

Average = __2__

6. 10, 6

$16 \div 2 = 8$

Average = __8__

7. 10, 7, 6, 9

$32 \div 4 = 7$

Average = __8__

8. 2, 8, 5, 9, 1

$25 \div 5 = 5$

Average = __5__

9. 7, 6, 14, 9

$36 \div 4 = 8$

Average = __9__

10. Fritha went to baseball card fairs each month of the summer. In June she bought 9 cards, in July she bought 15, and in August she bought 6. What was the average number of cards she bought each month? ___10___

11. Lindsay wrote four e-mails on Monday, five on Tuesday, three on Wednesday, and four each on Thursday and Friday. What was the average number of e-mails written each day? __20__ = 4

4   5   3   4 4

12. Kym read in her book each day for six days. She read the following numbers of pages each day: 8, 6, 5, 10, 13, and 12. What is the average number of pages she read each day? __9__

Find the average of the given numbers.

1. 2, 5, 5
   $12 \div 3 = 4$

2. 10, 5, 9
   $24 \div 3 = 8$

3. 11, 6, 10
   $27 \div 3 = 9$

Average = 4

Average = 8

Average = 9

4. 2, 8
   $10 \div 2 = 5$

5. 7, 9, 14, 6
   $36 \div 4 = 9$

6. 7, 5
   $12 \div 2 = 6$

Average = 5

Average = 9

Average = 6

7. 10, 3, 6, 1
   $20 \div 4 = 5$

8. 8, 5, 8, 7
   $26 \div 4 = 6$

9. 3, 3, 6, 9, 9
   $30 \div 5 =$

Average = 5

Average = 6

Average = 6

10. Julia, the jewel collector, found 10 gems in the first mine, 11 in the second, 9 in the third, and 10 in the fourth. What was the average number of jewels per mine? _____

11. Ben's vehicles needed some serious repairs. His motorcycle needed 8 new parts, his four wheeler needed 7 new parts, his car needed 10, and his truck needed 7. What was the average number of defective parts per vehicle? _____

12. The amount of rainfall for each of the last six months is as follows: 8 in, 7 in, 4 in, 10 in, 9 in, and 10 in. What was the average monthly rainfall during the last six months? _____

Find the average of the given numbers.

1. 8, 10, 12

2. 7, 6, 8

3. 1, 2, 6

Average = ____

Average = ____

Average = ____

4. 1, 5

5. 1, 3, 4, 8

6. 6, 8

Average = ____

Average = ____

Average = ____

7. 1, 3, 6, 7, 13

8. 4, 2, 6, 8

9. 9, 12, 2, 5

Average = ____

Average = ____

Average = ____

10. Andrew made 9 points in the first quarter, 12 points in the second quarter, 8 in the third, and 11 in the fourth. What was his per-quarter average for the basketball game? __10__

$9+12+8+11=\frac{40}{4}=10$

11. Jimmy sold 10 tickets for the play on Monday, 9 on Tuesday, 12 on Wednesday, 5 on Thursday, and 9 on Friday. What are his average daily sales? __9__

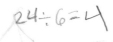

12. The amount of snow that fell in each of the last six months is as follows: 2 in, 3 in, 4 in, 6 in, 8 in, and 1 in. What was the average monthly snowfall during the last six months? __4__

$24 \div 6 = 4$

Find the average of the given numbers.

1. 2, 1, 3, 6 $12 \div 4 = 3$ Average = 3

2. 5, 7, 3, 10, 15 $40 \div 5 = 8$ Average = 8

3. 9, 4, 5 $18 \div 3 = 6$ Average = 6

Solve for the unknown to review the seven and eight times tables.

4. 7D = 49   5. 8D = 48   6. 7D = 56

Divide. Write your product under the number in the box.

7. $9\overline{\smash{)}36}$ → 6

8. $5\overline{\smash{)}50}$ → 10

9. $6\overline{\smash{)}42}$ → 4

10. $18 \div 2 =$ 9   11. $63 \div 9 =$ 7   12. $\dfrac{30}{6} =$ 5

Follow the signs.

13.   7 2   14.   1 5   15.   2 8
      - 3 4   x 4 7   x 1 8
      ─────   ─────   ─────
        3 8   1 0 5   1 8 2
                        + 6 0 0   + 2 8 0
                         ─────   ─────
                          7 0 5   4 6 2

Find the area.

16.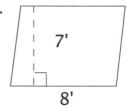

A = <u>63 sq.'</u>

17.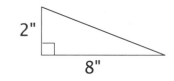

A = <u>16 sq "</u>

18. Jacob's mother said he watched too much TV. On Monday he watched three hours, on Tuesday two hours, on Wednesday three, on Thursday five, and on Friday two hours. What is Jacob's average daily number of hours spent watching TV? _____

19. Tom needs 24 quarts of paint. How many gallons should he buy?
   _____

20. Does the uppercase letter L demonstrate parallel or perpendicular lines? _____

Find the average of the given numbers.

   1. 9, 6, 7, 2   Average = ____

   2. 1, 3, 9, 8, 7, 8   Average = ____

   3. 8, 6, 13   Average = ____

Solve for the unknown to review the seven and eight times tables.

   4. $8D = 64$ 5. $7D = 63$ 6. $8D = 40$

Divide. Write your product under the number in the box.

   7. $9 \overline{\smash{)}27}$ 8. $9 \overline{\smash{)}72}$ 9. $2 \overline{\smash{)}4}$

   10. $45 \div 9 =$ ____   11. $18 \div 6 =$ ____   12. $\dfrac{70}{10} =$ ____

Follow the signs.

   13. $\begin{array}{r} 37 \\ \times\,17 \\ \hline \end{array}$ 14. $\begin{array}{r} 48 \\ -\,21 \\ \hline \end{array}$ 15. $\begin{array}{r} 53 \\ -\,29 \\ \hline \end{array}$

Find the area.

16.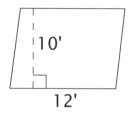

A = _____

17.

A = _____

18. Levi has a stack of 36 quarters. How many dollars does he have? _____

19. A teacher found she had 29 stickers left on one sheet and 25 on another sheet. If she divides the stickers evenly among nine students, how many stickers will each person receive? _____

20. The scientist counted 56 tentacles in the aquarium where he kept octopuses. Since each octopus has eight tentacles, how many octopuses were present in the aquarium? _____

Find the average of the given numbers.

1. 3, 4, 5, 4   Average = ____

2. 1, 1, 2, 3, 3   Average = ____

3. 4, 7, 4   Average = ____

Solve for the unknown to review the seven and eight times tables.

4. $8D = 72$ 5. $7D = 56$ 6. $7D = 49$

Divide. Write your product under the number in the box.

7. $9\overline{)18}$ 8. $6\overline{)12}$ 9. $6\overline{)54}$

10. $25 \div 5 =$ ____   11. $80 \div 10 =$ ____   12. $\dfrac{81}{9} =$ ____

Follow the signs.

13.   5 5
     x 2 7

14.   6 2
     x 3 8

15.   9 5
     - 4 6

Find the area.

16. 8"

8"

A = _____

17. 1 mi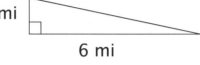

6 mi

A = _____

18. June needs 30 feet of fabric to make curtains. How many yards of fabric should she buy? _____

19. June bought nine yards of trim for her curtains. When she finished the job, she had five feet of trim left over. How many feet did she use for her curtains? (Hint: start by changing yards to feet.) _____

20. Name at least one uppercase letter that includes parallel lines.

_____

Answer the questions.

1. How many eights can you count out of twenty-four? _3_

2. How many sevens can you count out of forty-nine? _7_

3. How many eights can you count out of sixteen? _2_

Divide. For all problems with boxes, put the product under the number in the box and subtract.

4.
$$7 \overline{)\ 5\ 6}$$
4 16
-8
48

5.
$$8 \overline{)\ 6\ 4}$$
5 14
-8
56

6.
$$7 \overline{)\ 4\ 2}$$
3 12
-7
35

7.
$$8 \overline{)\ 4\ 0}$$
3 10
-5
35

8.
$$8 \overline{)\ 3\ 2}$$
2 12
-4
28

9.
$$7 \overline{)\ 6\ 3}$$
5 13
-9
54

10. $56 \div 8 =$ __7__   11. $35 \div 7 =$ __5__

12. $48 \div 8 =$ __6__   13. $\dfrac{28}{7} =$ __4__

14. $\dfrac{21}{7} =$ __3__   15. $\dfrac{72}{8} =$ __9__

16. Sarah works eight hours a week. When Sarah has worked 56 hours, how many weeks will she have worked? __7__

17. Anna has 14 cookies. If she divides them among seven friends, how many cookies will each friend receive? __2__

18. An octopus has eight tentacles. How many of the creatures are there if you count 48 tentacles? __6__

Answer the questions.

1. How many sevens can you count out of sixty-three? _____

2. How many eights can you count out of sixty-four? _____

3. How many sevens can you count out of forty-two? _____

Divide. For all problems with boxes, put the product under the number in the box and subtract.

4. $7\overline{|7\,0}$　　　　　　　　5. $8\overline{|2\,4}$

6. $7\overline{|4\,9}$　　　　　　　　7. $8\overline{|4\,8}$

8. $8\overline{|8}$　　　　　　　　　9. $7\overline{|5\,6}$

10. $40 \div 8 =$ _____

11. $28 \div 7 =$ _____

12. $72 \div 8 =$ _____

13. $\dfrac{21}{7} =$ _____

14. $\dfrac{35}{7} =$ _____

15. $\dfrac{56}{8} =$ _____

16. On his bike ride through the countryside, Thomas managed to cover eight miles every hour. If he covered 32 miles in all, how many hours did his ride take him? _____

17. Daniel Boone went on a hunting trip that lasted for 56 days. How many weeks was he away? _____

18. A carpenter has a piece of wood trim that is 63 inches long. If he cuts it into seven equal pieces, how long will each piece be?

_____

Answer the questions.

1. How many eights can you count out of fifty-six? __7__

2. How many sevens can you count out of fifty-six? __8__

3. How many eights can you count out of seventy-two? __9__

Divide. For all problems with boxes, put the product under the number in the box and subtract.

4.
$$\begin{array}{r} 9 \\ 7\,\overline{\smash{\big)}\,6\,3} \\ \underline{6\,3} \\ 0 \end{array}$$

5.
$$\begin{array}{r} 4 \\ 8\,\overline{\smash{\big)}\,3\,2} \\ \underline{3\,2} \\ 0 \end{array}$$

6.
$$\begin{array}{r} 3 \\ 7\,\overline{\smash{\big)}\,2\,1} \\ \underline{2\,1} \\ 0 \end{array}$$

7.
$$\begin{array}{r} 8 \\ 8\,\overline{\smash{\big)}\,6\,4} \\ \underline{6\,4} \\ 0 \end{array}$$

8.
$$\begin{array}{r} 3 \\ 8\,\overline{\smash{\big)}\,2\,4} \\ \underline{2\,4} \\ 0 \end{array}$$

9.
$$\begin{array}{r} 7 \\ 7\,\overline{\smash{\big)}\,4\,9} \\ \underline{4\,9} \\ 0 \end{array}$$

10. $16 \div 8 =$ _2_

11. $42 \div 7 =$ _6_

12. $40 \div 8 =$ _5_

13. $\dfrac{35}{7} =$ _5_

14. $\dfrac{14}{7} =$ _2_

15. $\dfrac{80}{8} =$ _10_

16. Seventy ants marched by in troops of seven. How many troops of ants marched by? _10_

17. Tim's message has 48 words. If he prints it on eight lines, how many words will be on each line? _9_

18. George walked the same number of miles every day. If he had walked 28 miles by the end of the week, how many miles did he walk in one day? _4_

Divide. For all problems with boxes, put the product under the number in the box and subtract.

1.
$$\begin{array}{r} 8 \\ 7\,\overline{)\,5\,6} \\ \underline{5\,6} \\ 0 \end{array}$$

2.
$$\begin{array}{r} 8 \\ 8\,\overline{)\,6\,4} \\ \underline{6\,4} \\ 0 \end{array}$$

3.
$$\begin{array}{r} 7 \\ 8\,\overline{)\,5\,6} \\ \underline{5\,6} \\ 0 \end{array}$$

4.
$$\begin{array}{r} 7 \\ 7\,\overline{)\,4\,9} \\ \underline{4\,9} \\ 0 \end{array}$$

5. $16 \div 4 = \underline{4}$

6. $36 \div 6 = \underline{6}$

7. $\dfrac{72}{9} = \underline{8}$

8. $\dfrac{21}{7} = \underline{3}$

Find the average of the given numbers.

9. 7, 1, 2, 6, 4   Average = $\underline{4}$

10. 10, 13, 9, 9, 8, 11   Average = $\underline{10}$

11. 6, 5, 13   Average = $\underline{7}$

Add. Regroup just as you did for two-digit numbers.

12.
$$\begin{array}{r} 1\,2\,4 \\ +\,3\,6\,9 \\ \hline 4\,9\,3 \end{array}$$

13.
$$\begin{array}{r} 7\,8\,1 \\ +\,3\,1\,9 \\ \hline 1,1\,0\,0 \end{array}$$

14.
$$\begin{array}{r} 3\,3\,5 \\ +\,1\,2\,6 \\ \hline 4\,6\,1 \end{array}$$

15.
$$\begin{array}{r} 4\,0\,4 \\ +\,2\,7\,8 \\ \hline 6\,8\,2 \end{array}$$

QUICK REVIEW

There are 16 ounces (oz) in one pound (lb). Check your pantry to find things that weigh a pound or close to a pound. Also, notice the unusual abbreviations for ounce and pound.

For now, we will be multiplying the number of pounds by 16 to find the number of ounces. Later we will be dividing by 16 to find the number of pounds when the ounces are known.

EXAMPLE 1   **Mary bought a five-pound bag of flour. How many ounces did it weigh?**

$$5 \times 16 = 80 \text{ oz}$$

16.   A brand-new baby boy weighs eight pounds. How many ounces does he weigh? _48 oz_

17.   Nathan paid for the book with 36 quarters. How much did the book cost in dollars? _8 dollars_

18.   John did yard work for Mrs. Martin. Last week he worked 3 hours, 4 hours, 2 hours, and 3 hours on different days. What is the average number of hours he worked each day? _3 hus_

19.   Each side of a square measures nine inches. What is the area of the square? _81 sq"_

20.   The path to Sam's front door is 18 yards long. How many feet long is the path? _6 ft_

Divide. For all problems with boxes, put the product under the number in the box and subtract.

1.
$$\begin{array}{r} 4 \\ 7\overline{\smash)28} \\ -28 \\ \hline 0 \end{array}$$

2.
$$\begin{array}{r} 6 \\ 8\overline{\smash)48} \\ -48 \\ \hline 0 \end{array}$$

3.
$$\begin{array}{r} 9 \\ 7\overline{\smash)63} \\ -63 \\ \hline 0 \end{array}$$

4.
$$\begin{array}{r} 6 \\ 7\overline{\smash)42} \\ -42 \\ \hline 0 \end{array}$$

5. $35 \div 5 = \underline{7}$

6. $27 \div 3 = \underline{4}$

7. $\dfrac{54}{9} = \underline{6}$

8. $\dfrac{56}{7} = \underline{8}$

Find the average of the given numbers.

9. 9, 4, 5, 6   Average = $\underline{6}$

10. 1, 2, 3, 4, 4, 5, 6, 7   Average = $\underline{4}$

11. 4, 5, 9   Average = $\underline{6}$

Subtract. Regroup just as you did for two-digit numbers.

12.
$$\begin{array}{r} 1\ 11 \\ 4\cancel{2}\cancel{1} \\ -208 \\ \hline 213 \end{array}$$

13.
$$\begin{array}{r} 3\ 12 \\ 6\cancel{4}2 \\ -127 \\ \hline 515 \end{array}$$

14.
$$\begin{array}{r} 6\ 18 \\ \cancel{7}\cancel{8}9 \\ -394 \\ \hline 395 \end{array}$$

15.
$$\begin{array}{r} 2\ 10 \\ \cancel{3}\cancel{0}3 \\ -163 \\ \hline 140 \end{array}$$

Find the area.

16.

2' 9'

$A = \underline{b \cdot h = 9}$
$\qquad\ \ 2$

17. In the last five years, Bill gained 25 pounds. How many ounces has he gained? __350 oz.__

```
   1
   18
 × 25
 ‾‾‾‾
  190
+260
‾‾‾‾
  350
```

18. Some days were better than others. Joelle made one mistake the first day, five the second day, ten the third day, and four the last day. What was her average daily number of mistakes? ___5___

```
   10
    5
    4
 +  1
 ‾‾‾‾
   20
 ÷  4
```

19. The gray squirrel buried 251 walnuts and 317 hickory nuts. The red squirrel stole 179 of the buried nuts. How many nuts does the gray squirrel have left in his stash? __399 nuts__

```
  251    568
+ 317   −179
‾‾‾‾‾   ‾‾‾‾
  568    399
```

20. Josh read 49 books during the last seven weeks. If he read the same number of books every week, how many books did he read in a week? ___7___

12F

Divide. For all problems with boxes, put the product under the number in the box and subtract.

1. $7 \overline{\smash{\big)}\ 3\ 5}$

2. $8 \overline{\smash{\big)}\ 7\ 2}$

3. $7 \overline{\smash{\big)}\ 1\ 4}$

4. $7 \overline{\smash{\big)}\ 2\ 1}$

5. $40 \div 8 = \underline{\hphantom{xx}}$

6. $16 \div 8 = \underline{\hphantom{xx}}$

7. $\dfrac{45}{5} = \underline{\hphantom{xx}}$

8. $\dfrac{64}{8} = \underline{\hphantom{xx}}$

Find the average of the given numbers.

9. 2, 4, 6, 8, 10   Average = _____

10. 1, 1, 2, 2, 4, 4, 5, 5   Average = _____

11. 4, 10, 16   Average = _____

Multiply.

12. $\begin{array}{r} 1\ 7 \\ \times\ 2\ 5 \\ \hline \end{array}$

13. $\begin{array}{r} 4\ 8 \\ \times\ 3\ 6 \\ \hline \end{array}$

14. $\begin{array}{r} 8\ 9 \\ \times\ 4\ 3 \\ \hline \end{array}$

15. $\begin{array}{r} 7\ 8 \\ \times\ 8\ 7 \\ \hline \end{array}$

Find the area.

16.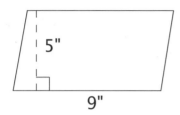

A = _____

17. Which package has more chips, the 1-pound package or the 20-ounce package? _____

18. Mildred prepared 18 pints of pickles. How many quart jars would hold them all? _____

19. Farmer Brown prepared 32 quarts of apple cider. He gave two gallons to Bobby for helping him. How many *gallons* of cider does Farmer Brown have left? _____

20. Margaret bought a case of pencils to pass out at her booth at the fair. The pencils were packaged 12 to a pack, and there were 24 packs in the case. How many pencils did Margaret buy? _____

Find the area of the trapezoids. The first one is done for you.
The drawings are sketches and may not be drawn exactly to scale.

1.

5'
8' / 4' 8'
9'

5 + 9 = 14

14 ÷ 2 = 7

7 x 4 = 28 sq ft

Area = ___28 sq ft___

2.

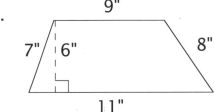

Area = _60 sq."_

3.

6'
5' / 4' 8'
10'

Area = _2 sq.'_

4.

6'
8' / 7' 8'
12'

Area = _63 sq.'_

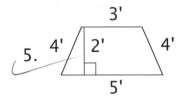

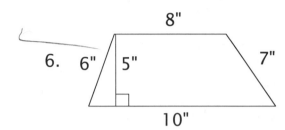

Area = _8 sq. '_

Area = _45 sq. "_

7. Austin cut shapes from colored paper to decorate the walls of his room. The trapezoids had bases of seven and nine inches and a height of five inches. What was the area of each trapezoid? _40 sq. "_

8. We visited a park that was shaped like a trapezoid. The bases measured one mile and three miles, and the height was two miles. What was the area of the park? _16 sq. mi._

Find the area of the trapezoids.

1.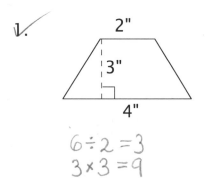

2"
3"
4"

$6 \div 2 = 3$
$3 \times 3 = 9$

Area = $\dfrac{b \cdot h = 9}{2}$

2.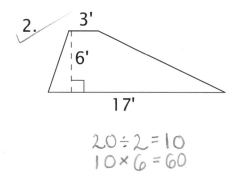

3'
6'
17'

$20 \div 2 = 10$
$10 \times 6 = 60$

Area = $\dfrac{b \cdot h = 60}{2}$

3.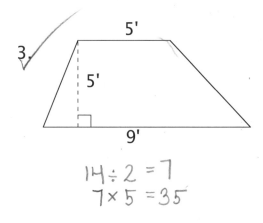

5'
5'
9'

$14 \div 2 = 7$
$7 \times 5 = 35$

Area = $\dfrac{b \cdot h = 35}{2}$

4.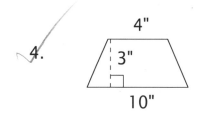

4"
3"
10"

$14 \div 2 = 7$
$7 \times 3 = 21$

Area = $\dfrac{b \cdot h = 21}{2}$

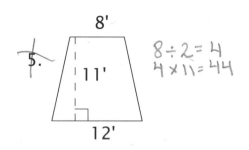

5. $8 \div 2 = 4$
$4 \times 11 = 44$

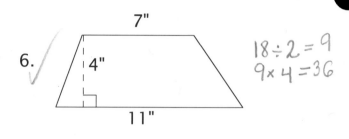

6. $18 \div 2 = 9$
$9 \times 4 = 36$

Area = $\dfrac{b \cdot h}{2} = 44$

Area = $\dfrac{b \cdot h}{2} = 36$

7. Pam's garden is shaped like a trapezoid. The bases are two and six feet long, and the height is six feet. The plants she plans to use need one square foot of space apiece. How many plants should Pam buy to fill her garden? __24 plants__

$8 \div 2 = 4$
$4 \times 6 = 24$

8. Richard designed a special book shaped like a trapezoid. The top of the book is five inches wide, the bottom of the book is seven inches wide, and the height of the book is six inches. What is the area of the front cover of the book? __36 in.__

$12 \div 2 = 6$
$6 \times 6 = 36$

Find the area of the trapezoids.

1.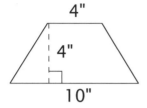

Area = _____

2.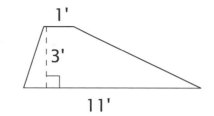

Area = _____

3.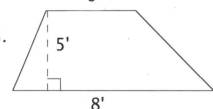

Area = _____

4.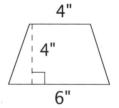

Area = _____

5.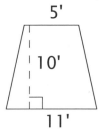

6.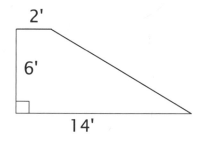

Area = _____

Area = _____

7. Sam walked one mile west, two miles south, and five miles east. From there, he headed back to his starting point. What is the area of the land that Sam walked around? _____

It may be helpful to draw a diagram and label it. The shape will be similar to that in #6.

8. An eccentric architect designed a room with a floor shaped like a trapezoid. Its bases were 6 feet and 14 feet and the height was 15 feet. How many one-foot-square tiles were needed to cover the floor? _____

Find the area of the trapezoids.

1.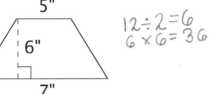

5"

6"

7"

$12 \div 2 = 6$
$6 \times 6 = 36$

A = ___36___

2.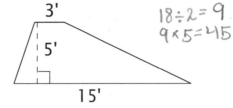

3'

5'

15'

$18 \div 2 = 9$
$9 \times 5 = 45$

A = ___45___

Divide. For all problems with boxes, put the product under the number in the box and subtract.

3. $9 \overline{) 27}$ 4

4. $6 \overline{) 36}$ 6

5. $7 \overline{) 28}$ 4

6. $5 \overline{) 45}$ 9

7. $56 \div 8 = \underline{7}$

8. $49 \div 7 = \underline{7}$

9. $\dfrac{16}{2} = \underline{8}$

10. $\dfrac{42}{6} = \underline{7}$

Find the average of the given numbers.

11. 6, 5, 7, 10   Average = ___7___

12. 2, 6, 1, 4, 3, 2   Average = ___3___

13. 1, 5, 15   Average = ___4___

QUICK REVIEW

When multiplying by a number that ends in zero, like 20 or 30, you can use what you know about place value to make the job easier. Cover the zero and multiply the remaining numbers, and then write zero after your answer to make the place values correct.

EXAMPLE 1 $\quad 8 \times 20 = 8 \times 2\,0 = 16\,0 = 160$

EXAMPLE 2 $\quad 22 \times 30 = 22 \times 3\,0 = 66\,0 = 660$

14. $7 \times 20 =$ _____   15. $13 \times 20 =$ _____   16. $9 \times 30 =$ _____

17. In order to have enough for all his horses, Lester bought 24 horse shoes. How many horses was he buying for? _6_

18. If it took Danny six minutes to play a song on his trumpet, how many songs could he play in an hour? (60 minutes) _10_

19. There are 12 months in a year. How many months old is a 20-year-old? _240_

20. Drew went to the store to buy a model-airplane engine, which cost $65. If he gave the cashier $90, how much change should he receive in return? _25$_

Find the area of the figures.

1.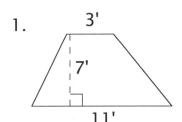

A = _____

2.

A = _____

Divide. For all problems with boxes, put the product under the number in the box and subtract.

3. $9\overline{)63}$

4. $9\overline{)72}$

5. $2\overline{)2}$

6. $3\overline{)18}$

7. $32 \div 4 =$ _____

8. $25 \div 5 =$ _____

9. $\dfrac{48}{6} =$ _____

10. $\dfrac{56}{7} =$ _____

Add or subtract.

11.
```
  1 7 8
+ 3 3 4
```

12.
```
  5 2 1
- 4 1 3
```

13.
```
  7 0 8
+ 2 2 2
```

Multiply using the shortcut method from 13D.

14. 9 x 20 = _____

15. 34 x 20 = _____

16. 11 x 30 = _____

17. Patty's business trip to Europe lasted 63 days. If she took one day each week to rest, how many days of rest did she have during the trip? _____

18. Scott has a 24-foot fence he would like to have painted. He asked each of his four children to paint an equal section of fence. How long a section will each person have to paint? _____

19. Kurt the dogcatcher rounded up 11 poodles, 15 beagles, 4 Saint Bernards, 10 bulldogs, and 5 collies and took them to the adoption center. How many dogs did Kurt bring in? _____ What was the average number of dogs per breed? _____

20. A baby weighs 13 pounds. How many ounces does the baby weigh? _____

Find the area of the figures.

1.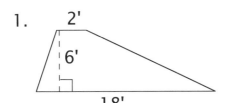

A = _____

2.

A = _____

Divide.

3. $7 \overline{)3\,5}$

4. $9 \overline{)3\,6}$

5. $6 \overline{)5\,4}$

6. $8 \overline{)6\,4}$

7. $48 \div 8 =$ _____

8. $24 \div 6 =$ _____

9. $\dfrac{50}{5} =$ _____

10. $\dfrac{21}{7} =$ _____

Fill in the blanks.

11. 16 qt = ____ gal

12. 36 quarters = ____ dollars

13. 24 ft = ____ yd

Multiply using the short cut method from 13D.

14. 6 x 30 = ____   15. 21 x 20 = ____   16. 42 x 30 = ____

17. Thirty-two people were expected to come to Vernon's party. If one cake was enough for eight people, how many cakes would Vernon need for all 32 people? _____

18. Greg wanted to collect quarters from all 50 states. He went to the bank and got 20 quarters. How many dollars did he have to exchange for the quarters? _____

19. When Greg got home, he was surprised and pleased to find that each quarter was from a different state. How many quarters does he still need to collect? (See #18.) _____

    Will $6 be enough to pay for the quarters he still needs? _____

20. Trisha wrote 419 words for her book report the first day she worked on it. The second day, she wrote 495 more words. How many words has she written in all? _____

14A

What number is represented? Give your answer in numbers.
The first one is done for you.

1. 1,000 + 400 + 10 + 8 __1,418__

2. 30,000 + 5,000 + 200 + 1 _____

3. 700,000 + 60,000 + 5,000 + 800 + 90 + 2 _765,892_

4. 4,000,000 + 200,000 + 60,000 + 5,000 + 100 + 40 + 3 _____

What number is represented? Give your answer in place-value notation.
The first one is done for you.

5. 2,356 __2,000 + 300 + 50 + 6__

6. 10,129 __10,000 + 100 + 20 + 9__

7. 195,328 _____

8. 1,786,201 _____

What number is represented? Give your answer in numbers.
The first one is done for you.

9. One thousand, five hundred forty-two 1,542

10. Twenty-eight thousand, six hundred sixteen _____

11. Four million, three hundred thousand, four hundred _____

12. Six million, eight hundred fifteen thousand, two hundred thirty-one _____

What number is represented? Give your answer in numbers.

1. 2,000 + 700 + 90 + 4 _____

2. 10,000 + 6,000 + 300 + 2 _____

3. 600,000 + 50,000 + 1,000 + 700 + 40 + 1 _____

4. 2,000,000 + 500,000 + 40,000 _____

What number is represented? Give your answer in place-value notation.

5. 7,801 _____

6. 41,456 _____

7. 238,199 _____

8. 5,365,000 _____

What number is represented? Give your answer in numbers.

9. Three thousand, twenty-one _____

10. Forty-five thousand, six hundred fifteen _____

11. Five million, four hundred thousand _____

12. Eight million, one hundred thirty-one thousand, five hundred twenty-eight _____

What number is represented? Give your answer in numbers.

1. 1,000 + 200 + 20 + 4 _____

2. 40,000 + 3,000 + 600 + 30 + 8 _____

3. 200,000 + 40,000 + 7,000 _____

4. 3,000,000 + 100,000 + 20,000 + 2,000 + 400 + 70 + 2 _____

What number is represented? Give your answer in place-value notation.

5. 3,256 _____

6. 50,604 _____

7. 754,753 _____

8. 2,117,249 _____

What number is represented? Give your answer in numbers.

9. One thousand, eight hundred thirty-eight _____

10. Thirty-three thousand, two hundred thirty _____

11. Two million, three hundred fifty thousand _____

12. Four million, six hundred fifty-two thousand, eight hundred ninety-three _____

Follow the directions.

1. Write using numbers: 1,000 + 600 + 50 + 2 ___1,652___

2. Write using place-value notation: 6,340,129 ___6,000,000 + 300,000 +___
   ___40,000 + 100 + 20 + 9___

Find the area of the figures.

3.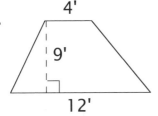

$16 \div 2 = 8$
$8 \times 9 = 72$

A = ___72'___

4.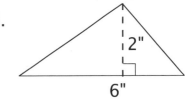

A = ___6"___

Divide. For all problems with boxes, put the product under the number in the box and subtract.

5. $7\overline{)42}$ ⁶

6. $6\overline{)54}$ ⁹

7. $9\overline{)81}$ ⁹

8. $8\overline{)40}$ ⁵

9. $14 \div 7 =$ ___2___

10. $12 \div 4 =$ ___3___

11. $\dfrac{15}{3} =$ ___5___

12. $\dfrac{70}{7} =$ ___10___

Cover the zeros and multiply. Then include the zeros after your answer to make the place value correct. The first one is done for you.

13. 6 x 200 = 6 x 2⟨ ⟩ = 12⟨ ⟩ = 1,200

14. 17 x 100 = _1,700_

$$\begin{array}{r} \times 100 \\ \hline 1,700 \end{array}$$

15. 8 x 200 = _400_

$$\begin{array}{r} \times 200 \\ \hline 400 \end{array}$$

16. Isaac had 478 marbles and lost 182 of them. How many did he have left? _296_

$$\begin{array}{r} 4\overset{3}{\cancel{7}}\overset{17}{\cancel{8}} \\ -182 \\ \hline 296 \end{array}$$

17. The Washington Monument is 555 feet high. How many feet would you travel if you went all the way to the top and back down again? _1,110'_

$$\begin{array}{r} \overset{1}{5}\overset{1}{5}5 \\ +555 \\ \hline 1,110 \end{array}$$

18. Mom made 24 cookies to be distributed evenly among the 4 boys. How many cookies did each boy get? _6_

Follow the directions.

1. Write using numbers: 20,000 + 5,000 + 600 + 10 + 1 _____

2. Write using place-value notation: 1,174,000 _____

_____

Find the area of the figures.

3.

2"

3"

4"

4.

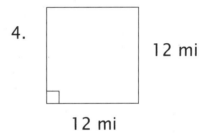

12 mi

12 mi

A = _____

A = _____

Divide. For all problems with boxes, put the product under the number in the box and subtract.

5. 5 ⟌ 3 5

6. 6 ⟌ 1 8

7. 7 ⟌ 2 8

8. 9 ⟌ 2 7

9. $72 \div 8 =$ ____

10. $20 \div 5 =$ ____

11. $\dfrac{8}{4} =$ ____

12. $\dfrac{12}{3} =$ ____

Cover the zeros and multiply. Then include the zeros after your answer to make the place value correct.

13. $23 \times 100 =$ ____

14. $14 \times 200 =$ ____

15. $9 \times 200 =$ ____

16. How many square feet are there in a bedroom that is 8 feet by 11 feet? ____

17. Lisa carried in 12 fireplace logs each day for 10 days. How many logs did she carry in so her family would have a nice, cozy fire? ____

18. Katie collected 14 quarts of raspberries, but Megan and Sarah ate 6 quarts of them. How many *pints* of raspberries were left for breakfast? ____

Follow the directions.

1. Write using numbers: 10,000 + 4,000 + 700 + 10 + 5 _____

2. Write using place-value notation: 4,711,340 _____

_____

Find the area of the figures.

3.

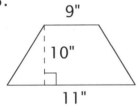

A = _____

4.

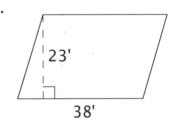

A = _____

Divide. For all problems with boxes, put the product under the number in the box and subtract.

5. 10 ⟌ 9 0

6. 9 ⟌ 1 8

7. 7 ⟌ 4 9

8. 6 ⟌ 4 2

9. $14 \div 2 =$ _____

10. $7 \div 1 =$ _____

11. $\dfrac{36}{6} =$ _____

12. $\dfrac{28}{4} =$ _____

Cover the zeros and multiply. Then include the zeros after your answer to make the place value correct.

13. $7 \times 200 =$ _____

14. $33 \times 200 =$ _____

15. $15 \times 100 =$ _____

16. Are railroad tracks parallel or perpendicular to each other? _____

17. Kia's little sister weighs 15 pounds. How many ounces does her little sister weigh? _____

18. Kendra earned these numbers of points each time she played her favorite game: 7, 15, 13, 9, 6. What was her average score?
_____

Write in standard notation (regular numbers) and read the number.
The first one is done for you.

1. 8 x 1,000 + 4 x 100 + 3 x 1 ___8,403___

2. 1 x 10,000 + 1 x 1,000 + 3 x 100 + 6 x 10 + 8 x 1 _11,368_

3. 3 x 1,000,000 _3,000,000_

4. 6 x 1,000,000,000 _6,000,000,000_

Write each number with expanded notation. The first one is done for you.

5. 9,476 _9 x 1,000 + 4 x 100 + 7 x 10 + 6 x 1_

6. 30,108 _3 x 10,000 + 1 x 100 + 1 x 8_

7. 2,542,000,000 _2 x 1,000,000,000 + 5 x 100,000,000 + 4 x 10,000,000 + 2 x 1,000,000_

8. 6,000,000,000,000 _6 x 1,000,000,000,000_

Write in standard notation. The first one is done for you.

9. Three hundred ten thousand <u>310,000</u>

10. Two million, one hundred thirteen thousand <u>2,113,000</u>

11. Seven billion, nine hundred forty-five million <u>7,945,000,000</u>

12. Two trillion, one hundred twelve <u>2,000,000,000,112</u>

Write in standard notation and read the number.

1. 5 x 10,000 + 9 x 100 + 4 x 10 _____

2. 6 x 100,000 + 7 x 10,000 + 2 x 1,000 + 8 x 100 _____

3. 9 x 10,000,000 + 4 x 1,000,000 _____

4. 2 x 1,000,000,000,000 + 6 x 100,000,000,000 + 4 x

    10,000,000,000 + 8 x 1,000,000,000 _____

Write with expanded notation.

5. 500,000,000,019 _____

6. 1,783,000,000,000 _____

7. 72,350,000,000 _____

8. 7,000,000,000,620 _____

Write in standard notation.

9. fifty-nine thousand, one hundred forty _____

10. one million, eighty-nine _____

11. thirty-two billion, four hundred seventy-seven thousand

_____

12. seven trillion, eight hundred ninety-one billion _____

Write in standard notation and read the number.

1. 6 x 10,000,000 + 6 x 1 _____

2. 4 x 100,000,000 + 9 x 10,000,000 + 5 x 1,000,000 +

    6 x 1,000 + 2 x 100 _495,006,200_

3. 3 x 10,000,000 + 6 x 1,000,000 _____

4. 3 x 1,000,000,000,000 + 3 x 1,000,000,000 _____

Write with expanded notation.

5. 725,078,000,000 _7×100,000,000,000 + 2×10,000,000,000_
    _5×1,000,000,000 + 7×10,000,000 + 8×1,000,000_

6. 40,316,000,000,000 _____

7. 1,465,900,000 _____

8. 371,800,000,000,000 _____

Write in standard notation.

9. Two hundred fifty-six thousand, ninety-four _____

10. Six trillion, eight hundred fifty-one million _____

11. Eight hundred seventy-four million, three hundred twenty

_____

12. One billion, sixty-seven million _____

15D

Follow the directions.

1. Write in standard notation and read the number:

   5 x 100,000,000,000 + 4 x 10,000,000,000 +
   7 x 1,000,000,000

   <u>547,000,000,000</u>

2. Write using expanded notation: 564,000,000,000,000

   <u>5×100,000,000,000,000 + 6×10,000,000,000,000 + 4×1,000,000,000,000</u>

Divide. Put the product under the number in the box and subtract.

3. 3
   7⟌21
     21
     ‾‾
     0 0

4. 5
   6⟌30
     30
     ‾‾
     0 0

5. 7
   8⟌56
     56
     ‾‾
     0 0

6. 5
   9⟌45
     45
     ‾‾
     0 0

Challenge: Write the correct sign (+, -, x, ÷) in each blank. The first one is done for you.

7. 24 <u>÷</u> 4 = 6

8. 3 <u>X</u> 5 = 15

9. 7 <u>+</u> 14 = 21

10. 14 <u>−</u> 7 = 7

Add just as you did for two- or three-digit numbers. If you have trouble keeping the numbers lined up, recopy the problems on a piece of notebook paper turned sideways.

11. $\begin{array}{r} 1,582 \\ +\ 3,624 \\ \hline 5,206 \end{array}$

12. $\begin{array}{r} 7,132 \\ +\ 5,333 \\ \hline 12,465 \end{array}$

13. $\begin{array}{r} 2,852 \\ +\ 4,263 \\ \hline 7,115 \end{array}$

Cover the zeros and multiply. Then write the zeros after your answer to make the place value correct.

14. 22 x 40 = 880
$\begin{array}{r} +40 \\ \hline 880 \end{array}$

15. 11 x 60 = 660
$\begin{array}{r} \times 60 \\ \hline 660 \end{array}$

16. 12 x 40 = 480
$\begin{array}{r} 40 \\ \hline 480 \end{array}$

17. The puzzle came with 200 pieces, but 17 are lost. How many pieces are left? 993

$\begin{array}{r} 200 \\ -\ 17 \\ \hline 193 \end{array}$

18. Our trip to Tampa, Florida, from Pennsylvania was 1,436 miles. On the way home, we came through Atlanta, Georgia, so the return trip was 1,529 miles. How long was our trip in all? 2,965

$\begin{array}{r} 1436 \\ +\ 1,529 \\ \hline 2,965 \end{array}$

Follow the directions.

1. Write in standard notation and read the number:

1 x 100,000 + 7 x 1,000 + 8 x 100 + 7 x 10 + 3 x 1

_____

2. Write using expanded notation: 3,000,000,000,500

_____

Divide. Put the product under the number in the box and subtract.

3. 7 | 5 6

4. 6 | 4 8

5. 5 | 3 0

6. 3 | 2 1

Write the correct sign (+, -, x, ÷) in each blank.

7. 8 __ 8 = 64

8. 16 __ 8 = 8

9. 64 __ 8 = 8

10. 8 __ 8 = 16

Subtract just as you did for two- or three-digit numbers.

11.   1, 4 2 6   12.   4, 2 8 3   13.   6, 2 4 1
     -    8 7 3   -   9 5 5   -   3 7 8

Cover the zeros and multiply. Then write the zeros after your answer to make the place value correct.

14. $14 \times 20 =$ ____   15. $20 \times 100 =$ ____   16. $45 \times 100 =$ ____

17.   Chad found the number of home runs the Boston Red Sox hit in May was 27, in June was 38, and in July was 34. What was the average number of runs per month? _____
(Use your blocks if you wish.)

18.   Craig sold homemade maple syrup for $6 a quart. If he sold 36 quarts, how much money did he make? _____

How many gallons of syrup did he sell? _____

Follow the directions.

1. Write in standard notation and read the number:

   8 x 1,000,000,000 + 4 x 100,000,000 + 7 x 10,000,000 + 2 x 1,000,000 + 6 x 100,000

   _____

2. Write using expanded notation: 2,027,000,000,000

   _____

Divide. Put the product under the number in the box and subtract.

3. 9 $\overline{)6\ 3}$

4. 8 $\overline{)2\ 4}$

5. 6 $\overline{)4\ 2}$

6. 7 $\overline{)4\ 9}$

Write the correct sign (+, -, x, ÷) in each blank.

7. 36 __ 4 = 9

8. 54 __ 9 = 6

9. 9 __ 9 = 18

10. 18 __ 6 = 12

Add or subtract.

11.　　6, 7 3 2
　　　　3, 1 5 2
　　　＋ 7, 3 2 1

12.　　5, 9 8 9
　　－　　6 3 2

13.　　5, 2 3 2
　　　　7, 1 1 1
　　　＋ 3, 7 6 5

Cover the zeros and multiply. Then write the zeros after your answer to make the place value correct.

14. 11 x 60 = ____

15. 21 x 40 = ____

16. 40 x 200 = ____

17. The bases of a trapezoid are 8 feet and 12 feet. Its height is 25 feet. What is the area of the trapezoid? _____

18. Olive wanted to lose weight. Her sister offered to pay her a quarter for every ounce she lost. If Olive lost two pounds, how many dollars did her sister pay her? (two steps) _____

Divide. The first one is done for you.

1.
```
        6 r. 2
  4 ) 2 6
      2 4
        2
```

2.
```
        5 r. 3
  4 ) 2 3
     -2 0
        3
```

3.
```
        8 r. 3
  7 ) 5 9
     -5 6
        3
```

4.
```
        1 r. 6
  7 ) 1 3
     - 7
        6
```

5.
```
        3 r. 6
  8 ) 3 3
     -2 7
        6
```

6.
```
        2 r. 5
  8 ) 2 1
     -1 6
        5
```

7.
```
        9 r. 4
  9 ) 8 5
     -8 1
        4
```

8.
```
        2 r. 2
  9 ) 2 0
     -1 8
        2
```

9.
```
        7 r. 1
  9 ) 6 4
     -6 3
        1
```

10.
```
        6 r. 3
  6 ) 3 9
     -3 6
        3
```

11.
```
        6 r. 4
  6 ) 4 0
     -3 6
        4
```

12.
```
        2 r. 1
  6 ) 1 3
     -1 2
        1
```

13.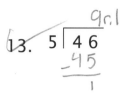

$$9r1$$
$$5\overline{)46}$$
$$-45$$
$$1$$

14. $$3r4$$
$$5\overline{)19}$$
$$-15$$
$$4$$

15. $$9r3$$
$$5\overline{)48}$$
$$-45$$
$$3$$

16. Jayne baked 75 cookies. She sold the same number to each of eight customers. How many cookies did each one get? __9__

How many cookies were left over? __3__

17. There are 13 apples in the refrigerator. If Laura eats two apples a day, how many days will they last? __6__

How many apples will she have left over? __1__

$$6r1$$
$$2\overline{)13}$$
$$-12$$
$$1$$

18. Mr. Smith has $48 in one-dollar bills. He wants to divide them evenly among his five children. How many dollars will each child receive? __9__

How many dollar bills will Mr. Smith have left over? __3__

$$9r3$$
$$5\overline{)48}$$
$$-45$$
$$3$$

188

DELTA

Divide.

1.
3 | 7
2r.1

2. 3 | 14
−12
2
4r.2

3. 3 | 29
−27
2
9r.2

4. 4 | 17
−16
1
4r.1

5. 2 | 9
−8
1
4r.1

6. 6 | 37
−36
1
6r.1

7. 7 | 29
−28
1
4r.1

8. 7 | 17
−14
3
2r.3

9. 5 | 51
−50
1
10r.1

10. 5 | 7
−5
2
1r.2

11. 8 | 66
−64
2
8r.2

12. 8 | 27
−24
3
3r.3

13.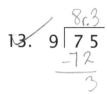

    8 r.3
    9 | 7 5
    -7 2
    ———
       3

14.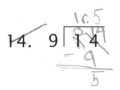

    1 c.5
    9 | 1 4
    -9
    ———
       5

15.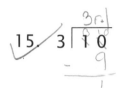

    3 r.1
    3 | 1 0
    -9
    ———
       1

16. Jayne wanted to try a new cookie recipe and had four friends over to sample the results. If she made 21 cookies, how many could each friend have? _5_

    How many cookies were left over for Jayne to eat? _1_

    5 r.1
    4 | 2 1
    -2 0
    ———
       1

17. Alice has 26 white rabbits. She has six hutches for them. If she puts the same number of rabbits in each hutch, will they fit evenly? _no_

    If not, how many extra rabbits will she have? _2_

    4 r.2
    6 | 2 6
    -2 4
    ———

18. Thirty-nine people want to play baseball. Since there are nine on a team, how many teams can be formed? _4_

    How many people will be left without a team? _3_

    4 r.3
    9 | 3 9
    -3 6
    ———
       3

Divide.

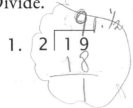

1. 2 | 1 9
   $\frac{9 \cdot \frac{1}{2}}{}$
   1 8
   ___
   1

2. 2 | 3

3. 5 | 1 6

4. 5 | 3 7

5. 9 | 7 6

6. 9 | 2 9

7. 4 | 3 8

8. 4 | 1 3

9. 7 | 9

10. 7 | 2 2

11. 3 | 1 6

12. 3 | 2 0   6r. $\frac{2}{3}$
    ^{10}
    - 1 8
    ___
    1 2

13. 8 ⟌ 1 9

14. 8 ⟌ 7 9

15. 6 ⟌ 5 0

16. There are 51 days left until Brenda's birthday. How many weeks and extra days is that?

_____ weeks and _____ days

17. Bill has $32. He wants to buy gifts for five friends. If he spends the same amount on each friend, how much can the gifts cost apiece? _____

How much money will Bill have left over? _____

18. Seventeen people need a ride to the museum. If five people can ride in one car, how many cars are needed for the trip? _____

Be careful with problems like this. You will need another whole car for the extra people, even if it's not full. You can't drive a part of a car!

16D

Divide.

1. $3 \overline{)23}$ 2. $3 \overline{)31}$ 3. $6 \overline{)20}$

4. $2 \overline{)11}$ 5. $4 \overline{)30}$ 6. $7 \overline{)40}$

7. $9 \overline{)57}$ 8. $5 \overline{)12}$ 9. $8 \overline{)43}$

Add or subtract.

10.	6,718	11.	5,302	12.	4,612
	+2,452		-1,238		-3,526

Cover the zeros and multiply. Then write the zeros after the answer to make the place value correct.

13. 11 x 700 = _____   14. 12 x 300 = _____   15. 20 x 500 = _____

16. Write using standard notation:

6 x 1,000,000,000 + 2 x 100,000,000 + 1 x 10,000,000 +
7 x 1,000,000

_____

17. Joseph needed 19 buckets of water for a wading pool. If he could carry two buckets at a time, how many full loads would he need to carry? _____

How many buckets would he take on his last trip? _____

18. A scientist counted 1,227 zebras and 2,341 antelopes on the African plain. How many animals did he count in all? _____

Divide.

1. $4\overline{)10}$

2. $7\overline{)45}$

3. $9\overline{)49}$

4. $6\overline{)46}$

5. $3\overline{)25}$

6. $8\overline{)50}$

7. $5\overline{)27}$

8. $2\overline{)5}$

9. $6\overline{)35}$

Add or subtract.

10.
$$\begin{array}{r} 2,482 \\ +7,902 \\ \hline \end{array}$$

11.
$$\begin{array}{r} 7,059 \\ +3,470 \\ \hline \end{array}$$

12.
$$\begin{array}{r} 6,997 \\ -2,961 \\ \hline \end{array}$$

Cover the zeros and multiply. Then write the zeros after your answer to make the place value correct.

13. 11 x 600 = _____   14. 13 x 200 = _____   15. 22 x 300 = _____

16. Write using expanded notation: 3,491,000,000,000

17. Wayne has $25 to spend on CDs. If each CD costs $8, how many of them will he be able to buy? _____

How much money will he have left over? _____

18. Debbie's weight-loss group is happy. The four women in the group have lost 20, 13, 8, and 7 pounds. What was their average weight loss per person? _____

Divide.

1. $2\overline{)7}$

2. $5\overline{)24}$

3. $8\overline{)62}$

4. $3\overline{)28}$

5. $9\overline{)88}$

6. $4\overline{)33}$

7. $7\overline{)65}$

8. $6\overline{)8}$

9. $7\overline{)53}$

Add or subtract.

10.
$$\begin{array}{r} 5,142 \\ -3,971 \\ \hline \end{array}$$

11.
$$\begin{array}{r} 9,065 \\ -4,018 \\ \hline \end{array}$$

12.
$$\begin{array}{r} 8,932 \\ +6,823 \\ \hline \end{array}$$

Cover the zeros and multiply. Then write the zeros after your answer to make the place value correct.

13. 10 x 700 = _____   14. 21 x 300 = _____   15. 22 x 400 = _____

16. Write using standard notation: seven million, three hundred forty-nine thousand

_____

17. Doris used three bows on every present she wrapped. If she had 26 bows, how many presents could she wrap? _____

How many bows would be left over when she was done? _____

18. We had a carpenter build two decks on our house. One deck is a rectangle 10 ft long and 8 ft wide. The other is a trapezoid with bases of 5 ft and 7 ft and a height of 6 ft. What is the area of the two decks combined? _____

Will a can of deck stain that covers 300 square feet be enough to stain both decks? _____

17A

Rewrite each problem using place-value notation, and then multiply.
Compare the answers you get using different methods.
The first two are done for you.

1.　　42　　　40 + 2
　　× 2　　　×　　2
　　　84　　　80 + 4

2.　　　2　　　　　2
　　× 42　　× 40 + 2
　　　　4　　　　　4
　　　80　　　　80
　　　84　　80 + 4 = 84

3.　　33　　　　×_____
　　× 3

4.　　　3　　　　×_____
　　× 33

5.　 431　　　×_____
　　× 2

6.　　　2　　　　×_____
　　× 431

Divide. The first two are done for you.

7.
$$
\begin{array}{r}
2\,0 \\
2\,\overline{)4\,0} \\
\underline{-4\,0} \\
0
\end{array}
$$

8.
$$
\begin{array}{r}
7\,0 \\
7\,\overline{)4\,9\,0} \\
\underline{-4\,9\,0} \\
0
\end{array}
$$

9. $5\,\overline{)1\,0\,0}$

10. $3\,\overline{)9\,0}$

11. $6\,\overline{)3\,6\,0}$

12. $4\,\overline{)1\,6\,0}$

Rewrite each problem using place-value notation, and then multiply. Compare the answers you get using different methods.

1.   3 2
    x 3   x _____

2.   3
    x 3 2   x _____

3.   4 3 8
    x   2   x _____

4.   2
    x 4 3 8   x _____

5.   1 2 9
    x   4   x _____

6.   4
    x 1 2 9   x _____

Divide.

7. $3\overline{)60}$

8. $9\overline{)810}$

9. $8\overline{)240}$

10. $2\overline{)80}$

11. $5\overline{)300}$

12. $7\overline{)210}$

Rewrite each problem using place-value notation, and then multiply. Compare the answers you get using different methods.

1. 2 5
    x 4   x _____

2.   4
    x 2 5   x _____

3. 1 2 2
    x   5   x _____

4.   5
    x 1 2 2   x _____

5. 1 2 4
    x   2   x _____

6.   2
    x 1 2 4   x _____

Divide.

7. $4\overline{)80}$

8. $6\overline{)420}$

9. $9\overline{)270}$

10. $3\overline{)120}$

11. $8\overline{)640}$

12. $5\overline{)350}$

Rewrite each problem using place-value notation, and then multiply.
Compare your answers.

1.　4 1 7　　　　　x _____
　　x　　2

2.　　　　　2　　　x _____
　　x　4 1 7

Divide.

3.　7 | 2 8 0

4.　6 | 1 8 0

5.　9 | 3 8

6.　8 | 6 7

Find the area of the figures.

7.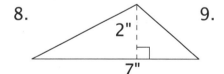

8.

9.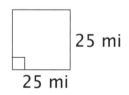

A = _____　　　　A = _____　　　　A = _____

Multiply or divide to fill in the blanks.

10.   5 lb = _____ oz

11.   20 quarters = _____ dollars

12.   12 qt = _____ gal

QUICK REVIEW

One ton equals 2,000 pounds. Use what you know about quick multiplying to find the number of pounds in the given number of tons. The first one is done for you.

13.   6 tons = ___12,000___ lb   (6 x 2,000 = 12,000)

14.   3 tons = _____ lb   15.   7 tons = _____ lb

16.   How many three-foot pieces can William cut from a board that is 16 feet long? _____

How long will the leftover piece of board be? _____

17.   John drove 312 miles each day for three days. Multiply upside down to find how far he drove in three days. _____

18.   Which contains more, a 2-pound can of spaghetti or a 30-ounce can of spaghetti? _____

Rewrite each problem using place-value notation, and then multiply.
Compare your answers.

1.   4 3 2
   x   5   x _____

2.   5
   x 4 3 2   x _____

Divide.

3. 5 | 4 5 0

4. 8 | 5 6 0

5. 4 | 1 3

6. 6 | 3 8

Find the area of the figures.

7. 1'
   6'
   7'

   A = _____

8. 3"
   4"

   A = _____

9. 5"
   7"

   A = _____

Fill in the blanks.

10. 8 lb = _____ oz

11. 18 ft = _____ yd

12. 24 qt = _____ pt

13. 5 tons = _____ lb

14. 9 tons = _____ lb

15. 4 tons = _____ lb

16. Billy's mother told him he could ride his bike around the block for 30 minutes. If it took him four minutes to go around the block one time, how many times could he go around the block without going over the time his mother gave him? _____

How many minutes will he have to spare after the last trip? _____

17. Mike made $112 a week. Multiply upside down to find how much he earned in four weeks. _____

18. Use expanded notation to write 5,643,700.

_____

Rewrite each problem using place-value notation, and then multiply.
Compare your answers.

1.
```
    3 4 1
  x     3    x  _____
  _____
```

2.
```
          3
  x 3 4 1    x  _____
  _____
```

Divide.

3. 2 | 6 0

4. 9 | 7 2 0

5. 7 | 4 5

6. 4 | 3 9

Find the area of the figures.

7.

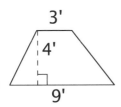

A = _____

8.

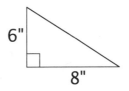

A = _____

9.

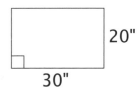

A = _____

Fill in the blanks.

10. 7 lb = _____ oz   11. 6 gal = _____ qt

12. 21 ft = _____ yd   13. 2 tons = _____ lb

14. 8 tons = _____ lb   15. 6 tons = _____ lb

16. Seventy-five people wanted to take a ride to the hotel in the airport shuttle van. If the van could carry nine passengers, how many loads would it have to take? (Be careful.) _____

   If the van took nine people in all but the last load, how many would be left to go in the last load? _____

17. Each bag held 231 jelly beans. Multiply upside down to find how many jelly beans are in three bags. _____

18. Use expanded notation to write six trillion, two hundred billion.

   _____

Divide and check your work by multiplying upside down.
The first two are done for you.

$$
\begin{array}{r}
2 \\
2\ 0 \\
1.\quad 4\,\overline{)8\ 8} \\
-8\ 0 \\
\hline
8 \\
-8 \\
\end{array}
\qquad
\begin{array}{r}
4 \\
\times\quad 2\ 0 + 2 \\
\hline
8 \\
8\ 0 \\
\hline
8\ 0 + 8 = 8\ 8
\end{array}
$$

$$
\begin{array}{r}
4 \\
2\ 0\quad r.\ 1 \\
2.\quad 2\,\overline{)4\ 9} \\
-4\ 0 \\
\hline
9 \\
-8 \\
\hline
1
\end{array}
\qquad
\begin{array}{r}
2 \\
\times\quad 2\ 0 + 4 \\
\hline
8 \\
4\ 0 \\
\hline
4\ 0 + 8 + 1 = 4\ 9
\end{array}
$$

3. $3\,\overline{)6\ 0}$

4. $\quad 2\,\overline{)4\ 6}$
$$
\begin{array}{r}
2\ 3 \\
2\,\overline{)4\ 6} \\
-4\ 0 \\
\hline
6 \\
-6 \\
\hline
0
\end{array}
$$

5. $3\,\overline{)6\ 7}$
$$
\begin{array}{r}
2\ 2\,r.\,1 \\
3\,\overline{)6\ 7} \\
-6\ 0 \\
\hline
7 \\
-6 \\
\hline
1
\end{array}
$$

6. $\quad 2\,\overline{)4\ 0}$
$$
\begin{array}{r}
2\ 0 \\
2\,\overline{)4\ 0}
\end{array}
$$

7.
$$
\begin{array}{r}
3\,2 \\
3\,\overline{)9\,6} \\
-9\,0 \\
\hline
6 \\
-6 \\
\hline
0
\end{array}
$$

8.
$$
\begin{array}{r}
4\ 1\,r.1 \\
2\,\overline{)8\,3} \\
-8\,0 \\
\hline
3 \\
-2 \\
\hline
1
\end{array}
$$

9. Daniel collects postcards. If he mounts two on each page in his scrapbook, how many pages does he need for 68 postcards?

34 pages

Multiply upside down to check your answer.

$$
\begin{array}{r}
34\,r.0 \\
2\,\overline{)68} \\
-60 \\
\hline
8 \\
-8 \\
\hline
0
\end{array}
$$

10. If there are 55 toes in the swimming pool, how many feet are in the pool? _11_

Multiply upside down to check your answer.

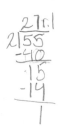

$$
\begin{array}{r}
27\,r.1 \\
2\,\overline{)55} \\
-40 \\
\hline
15 \\
-14 \\
\hline
1
\end{array}
$$

$5R=55$

$$
\begin{array}{r}
11 \\
5\,\overline{)55}
\end{array}
$$

Divide and check your work by multiplying upside down.

1.
$$\begin{array}{r} 23 \\ 2\,\overline{)46} \\ -40 \\ \hline 6 \\ -6 \\ \hline 0 \end{array}$$

2.
$$\begin{array}{r} 21\,r3 \\ 4\,\overline{)87} \\ -80 \\ \hline 7 \\ -4 \\ \hline 3 \end{array}$$

3.
$$\begin{array}{r} 21\,r2 \\ 3\,\overline{)65} \\ -60 \\ \hline 5 \\ -3 \\ \hline 2 \end{array}$$

4.
$$\begin{array}{r} 11 \\ 2\,\overline{)22} \\ -20 \\ \hline 2 \\ -2 \\ \hline 0 \end{array}$$

5.
$$\begin{array}{r} 32 \\ 2\,\overline{)64} \\ -60 \\ \hline 4 \\ -4 \\ \hline 0 \end{array}$$

6.
$$\begin{array}{r} 3\,r1 \\ 3\,\overline{)91} \\ -90 \\ \hline 1 \end{array}$$

7.
$$\begin{array}{r} 11\,r1 \\ 4\,\overline{)45} \\ -40 \\ \hline 5 \\ -4 \\ \hline 1 \end{array}$$

8.
$$\begin{array}{r} 44 \\ 2\,\overline{)88} \\ -80 \\ \hline 8 \\ -8 \\ \hline 0 \end{array}$$

9. Emaleigh has 66 jelly beans. If she divides the jelly beans evenly among herself and five friends, how many jelly beans will each person have? __11 jb.__

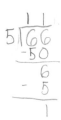

$$
\begin{array}{r}
1\ 1 \\
5\overline{)66} \\
-50 \\
\hline
6 \\
-\ 5 \\
\hline
1
\end{array}
$$

10. Chadwick loves the roller coaster. If he has 35 tokens and each ride costs 3 tokens, how many times will he be able to ride? __11__

How many tokens will be left over after the last ride? __2__

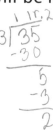

$$
\begin{array}{r}
1\ 1r.2 \\
3\overline{)35} \\
-30 \\
\hline
5 \\
-3 \\
\hline
2
\end{array}
$$

Divide and check your work by multiplying upside down.

1. 7 | 7 7
11
−70
7
−7
0

2. 5 | 5 8
11 r.3
−50
8
−5
3

3. 2 | 2 5
12 r.1
−20
5
−4
1

4. 3 | 3 7
12 r.1
−30
7
−6
1

5. 4 | 8 1
20 r.1
−80
1

6. 2 | 6 0
30
−60
0

7. 8 | 8 7
10 r 7
−80
7

8. 3 | 9 8
32 r.2
−90
8
−6
2

9. Kelsey sold 48 quarts of lemonade one hot day. How many gallons of lemonade did she sell? __12__

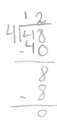

10. Briley has $99 to buy books. If each book costs $8, how many can she buy? __12__

How much money would she have left over if she bought that many books? __3__

$$
\begin{array}{r}
1\ 2\ r.3 \\
8\overline{\smash)99} \\
-80 \\
\hline
1\ 9 \\
-1\ 6 \\
\hline
3
\end{array}
$$

Divide. Check your work by multiplying upside down.

1.
```
     1 1 r.1
3 | 3 4
   -30
     4
    -3
     1
```

2.
```
     2 2 r.1
4 | 8 9
   -80
     9
    -8
     1
```

3.
```
    1 0 r 4
6 | 6 4
   -60
     4
```

4.
```
     7 r.1
8 | 5 7
   -56
     1
```

5.
```
    9 r 3
4 | 3 9
   -36
     3
```

6.
```
    4 0
7 | 2 8 0
   280
       0
```

Write the numbers in columns and add.

7. 16 + 25 + 48 = __89__

```
  +16
  +25
   48
   89
```

8. 423 + 32 + 7 = __462__

```
  423
   32
  + 7
  462
```

9. 8 + 2 + 1 + 9 = __20__

```
   9
   8
  +2
  20
```

Fill in the blanks.

10. 2 tons = __4,000__ lb

11. 10 tons = __20,000__ lb

12. 7 tons = __14,000__ lb

QUICK REVIEW

One mile (mi) equals 5,280 feet. Multiply to find how many feet are in the given number of miles. These are just like three-digit multiplication problems carried one more step. The first one is done for you.

13. 3 miles = __1 5,8 4 0__ feet

```
  5,2 8 0
x       3
        2
1 5,6 4 0
1 5,8 4 0
```

14. 2 mi = __1,0560__ ft

```
  5,280
x     2
1,0560
```

15. 8 mi = __4,1610__ ft

```
  5,280
x     8
4,1610
```

16. How many eight-inch pieces of ribbon can Stacia cut from a piece of ribbon that is 88 inches long? __11__

```
  11
8)88
-80
   8
```

17. Jenna drove four miles to work. How many feet did she drive?

21,160

```
  3
  5,280
x     4
21,160
```

```
  5,280
  4,618
41,610
+5,2800
  410
```

18. Marissa drove 2,465 miles on the way to the town where she spent her vacation. On the way home, she took a shorter route and drove 2,153 miles. How far did Marissa drive in all? __4,618__

```
  2,465
+ 2,153
  4,618
```

```
  5,280
x 4,618
  4,610
41,610
  5,280
```

Divide. Check your work by multiplying upside down.

1. $2\overline{)28}$

2. $3\overline{)61}$

3. $7\overline{)79}$

4. $5\overline{)11}$

5. $9\overline{)84}$

6. $6\overline{)240}$

Write the numbers in columns and add.

7. $6 + 4 + 3 + 2 + 9 =$ ____

8. $167 + 4 + 58 =$ ____

9. $11 + 15 + 41 =$ ____

Fill in the blanks.

10. 4 tons = _____ lb

11. 36 yd = _____ ft

12. 18 qt = _____ pt

13. 5 miles = _____ feet

14. 10 mi = _____ ft

15. 7 mi = _____ ft

16. Jared arranged 41 blocks in four equal rows. How many blocks were in each row? _____

How many blocks were left over? _____

17. Jordan needs to deliver 72 tons of feed to a farmer. If he can carry six tons of feed in his truck at one time, how many trips will he have to make? _____

How many pounds will one load of feed weigh? _____

18. Seven brothers and sisters had the following numbers of children: 2, 2, 0, 8, 4, 3, and 2. What is the average number of children per family? _____

Divide. Check your work by multiplying upside down.

1. $5 \overline{\smash{)}54}$

2. $8 \overline{\smash{)}81}$

3. $2 \overline{\smash{)}84}$

4. $3 \overline{\smash{)}16}$

5. $4 \overline{\smash{)}23}$

6. $9 \overline{\smash{)}720}$

Write the numbers in columns and add.

7. 245 + 961 + 102 = ___

8. 25 + 631 + 40 = ___

9. 9 + 8 + 6 + 2 + 4 = ___

Fill in the blanks.

10. 3 tons = _____ lb

11. 76 dollars = _____ quarters

12. 11 lb = _____ oz

13. 4 miles = _____ feet

14. 9 mi = _____ ft

15. 6 mi = _____ ft

16. Alexa's favorite bread recipe calls for four cups of flour. If she has 15 cups of flour on hand, how many batches of bread will she be able to make? _____

   How many cups of flour will be left over? _____

17. Kayla babysits for her neighbor. She worked 12 hours in January, 8 hours in February, and 16 hours in March. What is the average number of hours she babysits in one month? _____

18. Emma took $150 on her vacation. She spent $55 on meals and $38 on souvenirs. How much money did she have left over?_____

19A

Divide and check your work by multiplying. The first two are done for you. If you have trouble keeping the numbers lined up, you may copy the problems on a piece of notebook paper turned sideways, and use the lines to help you.

```
          6
          0
        1 0 0              4
1.  4 | 4 2 4           x 1 0 6
      - 4 0 0             2 4
        2 4                 0
        - 0             4 0 0
        2 4             4 2 4
      - 2 4
```

```
          3
        4 0  r. 1          6
2.  6 | 2 5 9           x 4 3
      - 2 4 0            1 8
        1 9            2 4 0
      - 1 8            2 5 8
          1            + 1
                      2 5 9
```

```
        2 1 3
3.  3 | 6 3 9
      - 6
        3
      - 3
        0 9
      - 9
        0
```

```
        3 4 3 r. 1
4.  2 | 6 8 7
      - 6
        8
      - 8
        0 7
      - 6
        1
```

```
        4 1 r. 2
5.  4 | 1 6 6
      - 1 6
        6
      - 4
        2
```

```
        3 0 6 r. 1
6.  2 | 6 1 3
      - 6
        1 3
      - 1 2
        1
```

7. Joe has collected 676 pennies. If he divides them evenly among six friends, how many pennies will each friend get? __112__
How many pennies will be left over? __4__

$$\begin{array}{r} 112\ r4 \\ 6\overline{)676} \\ -6 \\ \hline 7 \\ -6 \\ \hline 16 \\ -12 \\ \hline 4 \end{array}$$

8. Eight hundred and forty-four antelope hooves galloped across the African plain. How many antelope were present? __211__

$$\begin{array}{r} 211 \\ 4\overline{)844} \\ -8 \\ \hline 4 \\ -4 \\ \hline 04 \\ -4 \\ \hline 0 \end{array}$$

Divide and check your work by multiplying.

1.
$$\begin{array}{r} 55\,r2 \\ 8\,\overline{)442} \\ -40 \\ \hline 42 \\ -40 \\ \hline 2 \end{array}$$

2.
$$\begin{array}{r} 113 \\ 3\,\overline{)339} \\ -33 \\ \hline 9 \\ -9 \\ \hline 0 \end{array}$$

3.
$$\begin{array}{r} 139\,r2 \\ 3\,\overline{)419} \\ -3 \\ \hline 11 \\ -9 \\ \hline 29 \\ -27 \\ \hline 2 \end{array}$$

4.
$$\begin{array}{r} 323 \\ 2\,\overline{)646} \\ -6 \\ \hline 4 \\ -4 \\ \hline 06 \\ -6 \\ \hline 0 \end{array}$$

5.
$$\begin{array}{r} 227\,r \\ 4\,\overline{)908} \\ -8 \\ \hline 10 \\ -8 \\ \hline 28 \\ -28 \\ \hline 0 \end{array}$$

6.
$$\begin{array}{r} 31\,r1 \\ 5\,\overline{)156} \\ -15 \\ \hline 6 \\ -5 \\ \hline 1 \end{array}$$

7. Our driveway is 333 feet long. Divide by the number of feet in a yard to find how many yards long the driveway is. _____

$$\begin{array}{r} 1\,1\,1 \\ 3\overline{)333} \\ -33 \\ \hline 3 \\ -3 \\ \hline 0 \end{array}$$

8. Six hundred and sixty-nine people are waiting to go on the most popular ride at the fair. If only six people can ride at one time, how many groups are waiting to go? |11

One of the groups will not have six people. How many will be in that group? 3

$$\begin{array}{r} 1\,1\,1 \\ 6\overline{)669} \\ -66 \\ \hline 9 \\ -6 \\ \hline 3 \end{array}$$

Divide and check your work by multiplying.

1.

$$\begin{array}{r} 105\,r.2 \\ 3\,|\,\overline{3\,1\,7} \\ \underline{-3} \\ 17 \\ \underline{-15} \\ 2 \end{array}$$

2.

$$\begin{array}{r} 117\,r.5 \\ 7\,|\,\overline{8\,2\,4} \\ \underline{-7} \\ 12 \\ \underline{-7} \\ 54 \\ \underline{-49} \\ 5 \end{array}$$

3.

$$\begin{array}{r} 111\,r.1 \\ 4\,|\,\overline{4\,4\,5} \\ \underline{-4} \\ 4 \\ \underline{-4} \\ 05 \\ \underline{-4} \\ 1 \end{array}$$

4.

$$\begin{array}{r} 66\,r.2 \\ 4\,|\,\overline{2\,6\,6} \\ \underline{-24} \\ 26 \\ \underline{-24} \\ 2 \end{array}$$

5.

$$\begin{array}{r} 110\,r.5 \\ 6\,|\,\overline{6\,6\,5} \\ \underline{-66} \\ 5 \end{array}$$

6.

$$\begin{array}{r} 91 \\ 9\,|\,\overline{8\,1\,9} \\ \underline{-81} \\ 9 \\ \underline{-9} \\ 0 \end{array}$$

7. Evan has 802 gallons of cider for sale. If he sells it in two-gallon jugs, how many jugs will he need? __401__

8. Haley raises white mice. If she can keep five mice in a cage, how many cages does she need for 550 white mice? __110__

Divide. Check your work by multiplying.

1. 4 | 4 3 5   108 r.3

2. check for #1

3. 6 | 2 6 6   404 r.2

4. check for #3

Add.

5.   2, 9 6 2
   + 3, 1 4 8
   ‾‾‾‾‾‾‾‾‾
     6, 1 1 0

6.   1, 2 5 0
   +   3 5 1
   ‾‾‾‾‾‾‾‾‾
     1, 7 0 1

7.   3, 0 7 6
   + 1, 9 4 2
   ‾‾‾‾‾‾‾‾‾
     5, 0 1 8

Fill in the blanks.

8. 6 tons = __12,000__ lb

9. 2 mi = __10,560__ ft

10. 8 mi = __42,240__ ft

11. Are the writing lines printed on notebook paper parallel or perpendicular? _parallel_

12. Write in expanded notation: 6,583,000,000,000

$6 \times 1,000,000,000,000 + 5 \times 100,000,000,000 + 8 \times 10,000,000,000 + 3 \times 1,000,000,000$

13. Write in standard notation: six billion, seven hundred, five

6,000,000,705

14. Casey flew 4,568 miles on her business trip last spring. Kiley had to fly 7,821 miles. How many more miles did Kiley fly than Casey did? _3,242_ mi.

$$\begin{array}{r} 7,821 \\ -\,4,568 \\ \hline 3,242 \end{array}$$

15. Todd was organizing dog-sled teams. He had 69 dogs and used 6 dogs per team. How many teams could he make? __11__

How many dogs would be left over when he was finished? __3__

$$\begin{array}{r} 11\ r.3 \\ 6\overline{)69} \\ -6 \\ \hline 9 \\ -6 \\ \hline 3 \end{array}$$

16. Jeremiah ordered three tons of sand for his sand box. How many pounds of sand did he receive? _6,000_

Divide. Check your work by multiplying.

1. 3 | 9 6 0

2. check for #1

3. 5 | 2 8 7

4. check for #3

Subtract.

5.   5, 8 3 2
   - 2, 1 7 4

6.   9, 0 6 7
   -   1 5 8

7.   4, 9 6 5
   - 3, 4 5 6

Fill in the blanks.

8. 20 quarters = _____ dollars

9. 32 qt = _____ gal

10. 16 pt = _____ qt

11. True or false: In most homes, the left and right sides of a doorway are parallel to each other. _____

12. Write in standard notation:

    3 x 1,000,000,000,000 + 4 x 100,000,000,000 + 8 x 100

    _____

13. Kate jogged for 639 feet. How many yards did she jog? _____

14. Stephanie took a three-mile run yesterday. How many feet did she run? _____

15. Kimberly and Allison were writing letters. Kimberly's first letter was 560 words long and her second was 237 words long. Allison wrote only one letter, but it was 850 words long. How many more words did Allison write than Kimberly wrote? _____

16. Chuck wants to order topsoil for his garden. He can buy three tons for the same price as 3,500 pounds. Which is the better buy? _____

Divide. Check your work by multiplying.

1. 4 $\overline{)817}$

2. check for #1

3. 2 $\overline{)402}$

4. check for #3

Multiply. The first one is done for you.

5.
```
      7 4 3
   x     2 2
      1 4 8 6
    1 4 8 6
   1 6, 3 4 6
```

6.
```
    4 6 1
  x 8 5
```

7.
```
    5 5 8
  x 3 9
```

Fill in the blanks.

8. 100 yd = _____ ft

9. 4 mi = _____ ft

10. 17 lb = _____ oz

11. Is the line that goes up and down the left side of your notebook paper parallel or perpendicular to the other lines? _____

12. How many weeks are there in 700 days? _____

13. Write in standard notation: one million, two hundred fifty-one thousand, six hundred twenty-one _____

14. Paula spent the following amounts on groceries during the last four weeks: $131, $155, $100, and $102. What is the average weekly amount she spends on groceries? _____

15. Donald's country store always kept 11 different kinds of jelly on the shelves. He had 10 jars of each kind when a customer's dog got into the store and broke 17 jars of jelly. How many jars of jelly are left? _____

16. Abigail is studying China. She learned that Shanghai has 11,859,748 people and that Beijing has 9,230,687 people. How many people in all live in these two cities? (You can do this if you are careful to line up place value and take your time!) _____

Divide and write the remainders as fractions. Continue to check by multiplying. The first two are done for you.

1.

$$3\overline{)520} \quad 173\tfrac{1}{3}$$

```
     173⅓
3 |520        x 173
  -300            9
   220          210
  -210          300
    10          519
    -9         r. 1
     1          520
```

2.

```
     107⅔
3 |323        x 107
  -300           21
    23          300
   -00          321
    23         r. 2
   -21          323
     2
```

3.

```
    50 4/7
7 |354
  -35
    4
```

4.

```
   100 5/9
9 |905
  -9
     5
```

5.

```
   70
6 |420
```

6.

```
   121 6/8
8 |974
```

7. Mrs. Greene has $435 to divide between her two children.
How much will each receive? _217_

(Write the remainders for all the word problems in this lesson as
fractions.)

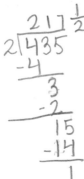

8. Shane has 185 feet of rope. How many yards of rope does
he have? _____

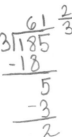

Divide and write the remainders as fractions. Continue to check by multiplying.

1. 6 | 2 5 0

2. 8 | 2 7 8

3. 4 | 2 1 4

4. 7 | 8 1 7

5. 6 | 6 5 8

6. 9 | 1 1 5

7. Andrew needs $145 to buy a desk for his room. If he can save only $7 a week, how many weeks will it take him to save the money he needs? _____

8. Farmer Jones has 253 bags of feed left for his animals. If he uses two bags a day, how many days will the feed last? _____

Divide and write the remainders as fractions. Continue to check by multiplying.

1. 8 | 7 6 2

2. 6 | 3 1 5

3. 7 | 2 3 6

4. 5 | 1 3 8

5. 2 | 3 4 1

6. 3 | 1 0 4

7. Alycia spent $124 buying eight books. How much did each book cost if the price was the same for each one? _____

8. How many four-gallon pails of water will Kent need to fill a 275-gallon tank with water? _____

20D

Divide. Write all remainders as fractions, and check your work by multiplying.

1. 6 | 8 4 7

2. check for #1

3. 5 | 1 0 4

4. check for #3

Use what you know about area and your division skills to find the missing side of each rectangle or square. The first one is done for you.

5. | 45 sq in | ?
    9 in

6. | 16 sq ft | 4 ft
    ?

7. | 14 sq in | ?
    7 in

? = __5 in__   ? = _____   ? = _____

Base (length) times height (width) equals area.

Solve for the unknown side by dividing the area by the given dimension.

$45 \div 9 = 5$, so height is five inches.

8. Sam flew his cargo plane 925 miles in two hours. How far did Sam fly each hour? _____

9. A cake is cut into 15 pieces. If it is divided evenly among six people, how many pieces will each person get? _____

10. An athlete runs eight miles a day. How many feet does he run each day? _____

11. Is the ceiling of your room perpendicular or parallel to the walls? (If you have a slanted ceiling, the answer is neither!) _____

12. Thirty-five tons of rock and earth slid down the hill after the storm. How many pounds came down in the landslide? _____

13. The high temperatures for the last three days were 63˚, 79˚, and 72˚. What was the average high temperature? _____

14. The low temperatures for the same three days were 41˚, 52˚, and 60˚. What was the average low temperature? _____

15. In 1912, Arizona became the 48th state to enter the Union. How long was that after 1787, when Delaware was the first state to enter? _____

Divide. Write all remainders as fractions, and check your work by multiplying.

1. 8 | 1 6 9

2. check for #1

3. 7 | 7 2 4

4. check for #3

Use what you know about area and your division skills to find the missing part of each parallelogram or rectangle.

5.

5"

?

area = 50 sq in

base = _____

6.

?

5 ft

area = 15 sq ft

height = _____

7.

?

9"

area = 72 sq in

height = _____

8. Heidi rode her bicycle at a steady pace for nine miles. If the trip took forty-five minutes, how many minutes did it take for each mile that she covered? _____

9. The packages Amy needs to mail each need five stamps. If she has 67 stamps, how many packages can she mail? _____

    How many stamps will be left over? _____ (This is a problem where a fractional remainder does not make sense.)

10. Sue set aside $350 to buy clothes for her eight children. If she spends the same amount on each, how much does she spend for each child? _____

11. How many ounces are there in one ton? _____

12. Courtney found that she had 486 quarters stashed away. How many dollars does she have? _____

13. Robert measured the distance between two parallel fences. If he measures the distance between them again at another point, should he get the same measurement? _____

14. The last two states to enter the Union were Alaska and Hawaii in 1959. How many years was that after Connecticut became a state in 1788? _____

15. Since there are 60 minutes in an hour and 24 hours in a day, how many minutes are there in a day? _____

20F

Divide. Write all remainders as fractions, and check your work by multiplying.

1. 4 | 7 2 5

2. check for #1

3. 9 | 4 6 7

4. check for #3

Use what you know about area and your division skills to find the missing part of each parallelogram or rectangle. All of these will have fractions in the answers.

5.   9"   area = 100 sq in   base = _____
     ?

6.   ? area = 25 sq ft   height = _____
     6'

7.   ? area = 59 sq in   height = _____
     8"

8. Mike's three horses ate a total of 528 pounds of hay in one week. How much did each horse eat if they all ate the same amount? _____

9. Driving at a steady speed, Marlin covered 444 miles in eight hours. How many miles did Marlin drive each hour? _____

10. Bethany ran two miles and Derrick ran 10,000 feet. Which one ran the farthest? _____

11. The price of coal is $315 for three tons. How much would one ton cost at that rate? _____

   Which is the better buy, $315 for three tons or $112 for one ton? _____

12. What is the area of a square that is 10 miles on each side? _____

13. How many perpendicular corners does a square have? _____

14. You are packing for a trip to Hawaii and the airline allows you two suitcases at 70 pounds each. You have 160 pounds of luggage. How much weight will you have to take in your carry-on bag? _____

15. Coming home from Hawaii (#14), you have 15 pounds of souvenirs as well as your luggage. How much over the weight limit for two suitcases are you now? _____

Round to the nearest ten.

1. 49 ≈ _50_   2. 22 ≈ _20_   3. 53 ≈ _50_

Round to the nearest hundred.

4. 631 ≈ _600_   5. 204 ≈ _200_   6. 862 ≈ _900_

Round to the nearest thousand.

7. 1,843 ≈ _2,000_ 8. 2,514 ≈ _3,000_ 9. 6,127 ≈ _6,000_

Estimate as explained in the instruction manual, and then divide and compare your answers. The first two are done for you.

10. $5\overline{)631}$ → $\begin{array}{r} 1\,0\,0 \\ 5\,\overline{)(6\,0\,0)} \end{array}$ 11. $\begin{array}{r} 1\,2\,6\,\frac{1}{5} \\ 5\,\overline{)6\,3\,1} \\ -5\,0\,0 \\ \hline 1\,3\,1 \\ -1\,0\,0 \\ \hline 3\,1 \\ -3\,0 \\ \hline 1 \end{array}$

12. $2\overline{)489}$ → ≈ 200 $2\overline{)(500)}$

13.

$$2\overline{)489} \quad 244\,r.\tfrac{1}{2}$$
$$\underline{-4}$$
$$8$$
$$\underline{=8}$$
$$09$$
$$\underline{-8}$$
$$1$$

14. $3\overline{)356}$ → ≈ 100 $3\overline{)(400)}$

15.

$$3\overline{)356} \quad 118\,r.\tfrac{2}{3}$$
$$\underline{-3}$$
$$5$$
$$\underline{-3}$$
$$26$$
$$\underline{-24}$$

16. A ship is 395 feet long. Estimate how many yards long the ship is, and then divide to find the exact answer. $\underline{100}$, $\underline{121\,r.\tfrac{2}{3}}$

$$3\overline{)395} \rightarrow \quad \approx 100 \quad 3\overline{)(400)}$$

$$3\overline{)395} \quad 121\,r.\tfrac{2}{3}$$
$$\underline{-3}$$
$$9$$
$$\underline{-9}$$
$$05$$
$$\underline{-3}$$
$$2$$

Round to the nearest ten.

1. 32 ≈ _30_   2. 67 ≈ _70_   3. 91 ≈ _90_

Round to the nearest hundred.

4. 384 ≈ _400_   5. 601 ≈ _600_   6. 745 ≈ _700_

Round to the nearest thousand.

7. 1,522 ≈ _2,000_ 8. 3,105 ≈ _3,000_ 9. 2,991 ≈ _3,000_

Estimate each answer, and then divide and compare your answers.

10. $2\overline{)735}$ → $2\overline{)(700)}$ ≈ 300   11. $2\overline{)735}$ 36 r. ½
        $\underline{-6}$
         13
        $\underline{-12}$
          15
         $\underline{-14}$
           1

12. $6 \overline{)487}$ → $6 \overline{)(500)} \approx 80$

13. $6 \overline{)487} \quad 81 \, r.1/6$
$\underline{-48}$
$\quad 7$
$\underline{-6}$
$\quad 1$

14. $9 \overline{)921}$ → $9 \overline{)(900)} \approx 100$

15. $9 \overline{)921} \quad 102 \, r.3/9$
$\underline{-9}$
$\quad 21$
$\quad 18$
$\underline{\quad\quad}$
$\quad 3$

16. Paul Bunyan's cook bought 938 gallons of maple syrup. If the syrup lasted eight days, how many gallons a day had the men used? Estimate, and then divide to find the exact answer. __100__ , __118 7/8__

$8 \overline{)938}$ → $8 \overline{)(900)} \approx 100$

$8 \overline{)938} \quad 118 \, r.7/8$
$\underline{-8}$
$\quad 13$
$\underline{-8}$
$\quad 68$
$\underline{-44}$
$\quad 7$

Round to the nearest ten.

1. 23 ≈ _____   2. 36 ≈ _____   3. 59 ≈ _____

Round to the nearest hundred.

4. 519 ≈ _____   5. 682 ≈ _____   6. 154 ≈ _____

Round to the nearest thousand.

7. 1,692 ≈ _____   8. 2,341 ≈ _____   9. 8,534 ≈ _____

Estimate each answer, and then divide and compare your answers.

10. 3$\overline{)436}$ →   3$\overline{)(\quad)}$ 11. 3$\overline{)436}$

12. $2\overline{)751}$ → $2\overline{)(\quad)}$ 13. $2\overline{)751}$

14. $5\overline{)845}$ → $5\overline{)(\quad)}$ 15. $5\overline{)845}$

16. A grocer has 820 quarts of milk in gallon jugs. How many jugs of milk does he have? Estimate, and then divide to find the exact answer. _____, _____

Fill in the blanks.

1. 78 to the nearest ten is __80__ .

2. 153 to the nearest hundred is __200__ .

3. 4,321 to the nearest thousand is __4,000__ .

Estimate the answer, and then divide and compare your answers.

4. 3 | 9 1 2 → ≈ 300 3 | (900)

5. 304 3 | 9 1 2
  - 9
  ‾‾‾
  12
  -12
  ‾‾‾
  0

Divide and check by multiplying.

6. 54 7 | 3 7 8
  - 35
  ‾‾‾
  28
  - 28

7. check for #6

8. $\overset{6\ 2 r./9}{9\ |\overline{559}}$

   -54

   19

   -18

   1

9. check for #8

Write each number in expanded notation.

10. 750,000 = $7 \times 100,000 + 5 \times 10,000$

11. 3,400,000 = $3 \times 1,000,000 + 4 \times 100,000$

12. 8,000,000,000 = $8 \times 1,000,000,000$

13. Billy put three oranges in each of the fruit baskets he made. If he had 24 oranges, how many fruit baskets could he make? ___8___

14. How many feet are there in 11 miles? __5891__

$$\begin{array}{r} 5,280 \\ \times \quad 11 \\ \hline 5,281 \\ + 5,2\ 810 \\ \hline 58,091 \end{array}$$

15. Holly and her two brothers each bought five greeting cards. How many greeting cards were bought in all? __15__

16. Uncle Carl has $375 to divide evenly among four nephews. How much money will each nephew receive? __93 r. 3/4__

$$\begin{array}{r} 93\ r.\ 3/4 \\ 4\ |\overline{375} \\ -36 \\ \hline 15 \\ -12 \\ \hline 3 \end{array}$$

Fill in the blanks.

1. 49 to the nearest ten is _____ .

2. 205 to the nearest hundred is _____ .

3. 6,512 to the nearest thousand is _____ .

Estimate the answer, and then divide and compare your answers.

4. $5\overline{)776}$ → $5\overline{)(\quad)}$ 5. $5\overline{)776}$

Divide and check by multiplying.

6. $4\overline{)225}$ 7. check for #6

8. $6 \overline{\smash{)}628}$

9. check for #8

Follow the signs.

10. 365 + 498 = _____

11. 863 - 125 = _____

12. 671 x 32 = _____

13. Rod got a box of chocolates for his birthday. There are 21 chocolates in the box. If he wants to make them last for a week, how many should he eat in a day? _____

14. How many pounds are there in 10 tons? _____

15. A classroom has an area of 70 square yards. If one side of the room measures seven yards, how long is the other side? _____

16. Give the dimensions of the room in #15 in feet. _____

Fill in the blanks.

1. 15 to the nearest ten is _____ .

2. 113 to the nearest hundred is _____ .

3. 8,099 to the nearest thousand is _____ .

Estimate the answer, and then divide and compare your answers.

4. $7\overline{)980}$ → $7\overline{(\quad\quad)}$ 5. $7\overline{)980}$

Divide and check by multiplying.

6. $3\overline{)463}$ 7. check for #6

8. $8\overline{)336}$

9. check for #8

Follow the signs.

10. 1,345 + 601 = _____

11. 4,532 – 2,055 = _____

12. 2,891 x 12 = _____

13. What is the area of a trapezoid with bases of 22 inches and 26 inches and a height of 19 inches? _____

14. A scientist studied the seed pods produced by a certain kind of plant. He counted the following numbers of seed pods on different plants: 58, 67, 91, and 88. What is the average number of pods per plant? _____

15. How many quart jars can be filled by 484 pints of honey? _____

16. What is the area of a triangle with a base of 15 feet and a height of 18 feet? _____

Divide, and then check by multiplying. Use estimation to help you
if needed. Write any remainders as fractions. The first one is done for you.

1.
$$21\overline{)715}$$
34 $\frac{1}{21}$
-630
85
-84
1

```
   21
 x 34
   84
  630
  714
  + 1
  715
```

2. $13\overline{)968}$
74 r. $\frac{6}{13}$
-91
58
-52

3. $12\overline{)785}$
65 r. $\frac{5}{12}$
-72
65
-60
5

4. $21\overline{)483}$
23
-42
63
-63

5. $11\overline{)638}$
58
-55
088
88

6. $15\overline{)377}$
25 r. $\frac{2}{15}$
-30
77
-75
2

11

7. A chef prepared 450 delicious treats for the banquet. If he plans to have 18 items for each guest, how many are invited to the banquet? __25__

8. The troops march 26 miles a day. How many days will it take them to march 390 miles? __15__

Divide, and then check by multiplying. Use estimation to help you if needed. Write any remainders as fractions.

1. $13\overline{)169}$ 13

2. $41\overline{)506}$ 12 r. $^{14}/_{41}$

3. $61\overline{)728}$ 11 $^{57}/_{61}$
    $\underline{-61}$
    118
    $\underline{-61}$
    57

4. $15\overline{)615}$ 41
    $\underline{-60}$
    15

5. $26\overline{)644}$ 24 $^{20}/_{26}$
    $\underline{-52}$
    1 24
    $\underline{-1 04}$
    020

6. $75\overline{)831}$ 11 r. $^{6}/_{15}$
    $\underline{-75}$
    81
    $\underline{-75}$
    6

7. Andrew put his collection of 315 stamps into small bags. If he put 15 stamps in each bag, how many bags did he need? _____

8. Wolfgang spends $732 a year on his hobby. How much is that per month? _____

Divide, and then check by multiplying. Use estimation to help you if needed. Write any remainders as fractions.

1.
$$
\begin{array}{r}
22 \\
12\overline{\smash)264} \\
-24 \\
\hline
24 \\
-24 \\
\hline
\end{array}
$$

2.
$$
\begin{array}{r}
21 \text{ r. } 2/14 \\
14\overline{\smash)386} \\
-28 \\
\hline
166 \\
-14 \\
\hline
2 \\
\end{array}
$$

3.
$$
\begin{array}{r}
43 \\
22\overline{\smash)946} \\
-88 \\
\hline
66 \\
-66 \\
\hline
\end{array}
$$

4.
$$
\begin{array}{r}
20 \text{ r. } 1/10 \\
10\overline{\smash)201} \\
-20 \\
\hline
1 \\
-0 \\
\hline
1 \\
\end{array}
$$

5.
$$
\begin{array}{r}
10 \text{ r. } 3/25 \\
25\overline{\smash)253} \\
-25 \\
\hline
3 \\
-0 \\
\hline
3 \\
\end{array}
$$

6.
$$
\begin{array}{r}
13 \\
38\overline{\smash)494} \\
-38 \\
\hline
114 \\
-114 \\
\hline
\end{array}
$$

7. Seven hundred thirty-five blackbirds swooped down on our yard. If 21 blackbirds sat in each tree, how many trees did they need?

_____

8. Douglas has $143 to spend on Christmas gifts. He wants to give books that cost $11 apiece. How many can he buy? _____

Divide, and then check by multiplying. Use estimation to help you if needed. Write any remainders as fractions.

1.
$$
\begin{array}{r}
23 \\
12\overline{)276} \\
-24 \\
\hline
36 \\
-36
\end{array}
$$

2. check for #1

3.
$$
\begin{array}{r}
29\ r.\tfrac{1}{24} \\
24\overline{)697} \\
-48 \\
\hline
217 \\
-216 \\
\hline
1
\end{array}
$$

4. check for #3

5.
$$
\begin{array}{r}
26 \\
3\overline{)78} \\
-6 \\
\hline
18 \\
-18
\end{array}
$$

6. check for #5

7.
$$
\begin{array}{r}
221\ r.\tfrac{3}{4} \\
4\overline{)887} \\
-8 \\
\hline
8 \\
-8 \\
\hline
7 \\
-4 \\
\hline
3
\end{array}
$$

8. check for #7

Find the area of each figure.

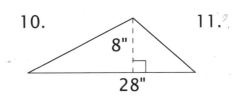

9. 10' 12' 32'
aug. is 21

252'

10. 8" 28"

112 sq.

11. 40 mi 40 mi

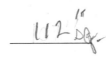
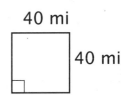

QUICK REVIEW

There are 12 inches in a foot. Look at a ruler to review feet and inches. Notice that when changing smaller units to larger units, you divide. When changing from larger units to smaller, you multiply. Carefully study the two that are done for you.

12. 48 in = __4__ ft

(48 ÷ 12 = 4)

13. 5 ft = __60__ in

(5 x 12 = 60)

14. 120 in = _____ ft

15. Alex has a rope that is 169 inches long. How many feet long is his rope? _____

16. Niall drove 25 miles. How many feet did he drive? _____

Divide, and then check by multiplying. Use estimation to help you if needed. Write any remainders as fractions.

1. 17 ⟌ 2 5 1

2. check for #1

3. 41 ⟌ 6 5 6

4. check for #3

5. 8 ⟌ 4 5

6. check for #5

7. 9 ⟌ 5 3 3

8. check for #7

Find the area of each figure.

9.
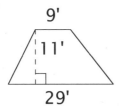
9'
11'
29'
_____

10.
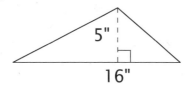
5"
16"
_____

11.
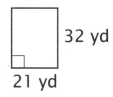
32 yd
21 yd
_____

12. 24 in = _____ ft   13. 10 ft = _____ in

14. 180 in = _____ ft

15. Brandon drove 576 miles. If he used 18 gallons of gasoline, how many miles did he go for each gallon? _____

16. Jonathon wants to be six feet tall when he grows up. How many inches is that? _____

17. Jeff ordered two tons of gravel for his driveway. How many pounds of gravel should he receive? _____

18. How many ounces of gravel should Jeff receive? (#17) _____

If he gathered up 32 ounces of gravel to use in flower pots, how many ounces were left for his driveway? _____

Estimate each answer, and then divide and compare your answers. Check
your final answer by multiplying. The first two are done for you. (The lines
are to help you keep your numbers in the right columns.)

1. $6\overline{)3689}$ → (6) $\overset{(600)}{)(4000)}$ 2.

6	1	4	$\frac{5}{6}$
6	3	6	8	9
-3	6	0	0
0	8	9
-6	0
2	9
-2	4
5

```
        6
    x 6 1 4
       2 4
       6 0
   3 6 0 0
   3 6 8 4
   +     5
   3 6 8 9
```

3. $5\overline{)1090}$ → 5 $\overset{200}{)(1,000)}$ 4.

```
        2 1 8
    5 1 0 9 0
     -1 0
        9
       -5
        4 0
       -4 0
```

5. $7\overline{)9479}$ → 7 $\overset{1,000}{)(9,000)}$ 6.

```
      1 3 5 4 r. 1/7
   7 9 4 7 9
    -7
     2 4
     2 1
       3 7
       3 5
         2 9
         2 8
          1
```

7. Noah divided 2,368 animals into groups of two. How many groups did he have when he was finished? 1,171 r. 8/2

$$
\begin{array}{r}
1\ 1\ 7\ 1\ \text{r.}\ 8/2 \\
2\overline{\smash{)}2,3\ 6\ 8} \\
-2 \\
\overline{3} \\
-2 \\
\overline{1\ 6} \\
-1\ 4 \\
\overline{2} \\
-2 \\
\overline{8}
\end{array}
$$

8. A store owner stocked 5,385 fly swatters. If his customers buy an average of five apiece, how many customers does he need to get rid of all the fly swatters? 1,077

$$
\begin{array}{r}
1\ 0\ 7\ 7 \\
5\overline{\smash{)}5,3\ 8\ 5} \\
-5 \\
\overline{3\ 8} \\
-3\ 5 \\
\overline{3\ 5} \\
3\ 5 \\
\overline{}
\end{array}
$$

Estimate each answer, and then divide and compare your answers.
Check your final answer by multiplying.

1. 9 | 6 0 6 3

$$\frac{600}{9\,|\,(6{,}000)}$$

2.
$$
\begin{array}{c}
6\ 7\ 3\ r.\ 6/9 \\
9\,|\,6\ 0\ 6\ 3 \\
-5\ 4 \\
6\ 6 \\
-6\ 3 \\
28\ 8\quad 13 \\
-2\ 7 \\
6
\end{array}
$$

3. 3 | 2 5 8 4

$$\frac{1{,}000}{3\,|\,(3{,}000)}$$

4.
$$
\begin{array}{c}
8\ 6\ 1\ r.\ 1/3 \\
3\,|\,2\ 5\ 8\ 4 \\
-2\ 4 \\
1\ 8 \\
-1\ 8 \\
4 \\
-3 \\
1
\end{array}
$$

5. 2 | 4 7 5 1

$$\frac{2{,}000}{2\,|\,(5{,}000)}$$

6.
$$
\begin{array}{c}
2{,}3\ 7\ 5\ r.\ 1/2 \\
2\,|\,4\ 7\ 5\ 1 \\
-4 \\
7 \\
-6 \\
1\ 5 \\
-1\ 4 \\
1\ 1 \\
-1\ 0 \\
1
\end{array}
$$

7. This spring, 1,125 new baby opossums were born in the forest. If each mother had nine babies, how many mother opossums were in the forest? __125__

$$
\begin{array}{r}
125 \\
9\overline{)1,125} \\
-\,9 \\
\hline
122 \\
-18 \\
\hline
45 \\
-45 \\
\hline
\end{array}
$$

8. Jim had 2,268 miles to drive in five days. How many miles should he drive each day if he wants to drive the same distance every day? __453 r 3/5__

$$
\begin{array}{r}
453\ r\ 3/5 \\
5\overline{)2,268} \\
-20 \\
\hline
26 \\
-25 \\
\hline
18 \\
-15 \\
\hline
3 \\
\end{array}
$$

23C

Estimate each answer, and then divide and compare your answers.
Check your final answer by multiplying.

1. 4) 6 0 2 2   4 (   )   2. 4 | 6 | 0 | 2 | 2

3. 7) 6 1 3 4   7 (   )   4. 7 | 6 | 1 | 3 | 4

5. 9) 2 5 1 6   9 (   )   6. 9 | 2 | 5 | 1 | 6

7. I saw 9,936 little legs crawling up a wall. The legs belonged to a swarm of ladybugs. How many ladybugs were crawling up the wall? (Insects have six legs.) _____

8. Michael has a mile-long fence to paint. If he wants to finish the job in four weeks, how many feet must he paint each day? _____

   Hint: First divide the number of feet in a mile by four, and then divide the result by seven.

Divide, and then check by multiplying. Use estimation to help you if needed. Write any remainders as fractions.

1. $\quad 4\,\overline{|1|5|3|8}$ → $3\,8\,4\ r.\,\tfrac{25}{4}$

2. check for #1

$4\overline{)3\,3}$

3. $\quad 3\,\overline{|4|3|6|0}$ → $1\,4\,5\,3\ r.\,\tfrac{1}{3}$

4. check for #3

5. $\quad 51\,\overline{|9|1|8}$ → $1\,8$

6. check for #5

$50\overline{)40\,0}$

$\begin{array}{r} 51 \\ \times\ 8 \\ \hline 408 \end{array}$

7. $\quad 38\,\overline{|4|2|2}$ → $1\,1\ r.\,\tfrac{4}{38}$

8. check for #7

$40\overline{)40}$

Multiply. The first one is done for you.

9.

	1,	8	5	4
x			2	5
	4	¹2	2	
	5	0	5	0
¹				
¹	1			
2	6	0	8	0
4	6	3	5	0

10.

	3,	7	3	6
x			3	1
	3,	7	3	6
+ 1	0	2,	0	8	0
1	0	5,	8	1	6

11.

	2,	9	4	5
x			6	3
	8,	8	3	5
+ 1	7	6,	7	0	0
1	8	5,	5	3	5

Fill in the blanks.

12. 600 ft = __1,800__ yd

$$\begin{array}{r} 600 \\ \times\ \ \ 3 \\ \hline 1,800 \end{array}$$

13. 48 pt = __96__ qt

$$\begin{array}{r} 48 \\ \times\ \ 2 \\ \hline 96 \end{array}$$

14. 16 qt = __64__ gal

$$\begin{array}{r} 16 \\ \times\ \ 4 \\ \hline 64 \end{array}$$

15. Is it sensible to say there are 485 hooves in a herd of cattle? _____

16. Alexandria drew a line on her paper, and then Paula drew another one parallel to it. Do the lines cross one another at any point? __no__

Divide, and then check by multiplying. Use estimation to help you if needed. Write any remainders as fractions.

1. 8 | 2 0 0 3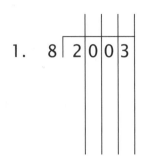

2. check for #1

3. 2 | 1 3 8 5

4. check for #3

5. 12 | 4 6 8

6. check for #5

7. 10 | 5 1 6

8. check for #7

Multiply.

9.
1,	3	4	8
×		2	9

10.
7,	5	3	9
×		1	2

11.
2,	0	0	0
×		5	6

Fill in the blanks.

12. 444 quarters = _____ dollars   13. 720 in = _____ ft

14. 80 oz = _____ lb

15. The hungry frogs snapped up the bugs. If they ate 2,067 in three hours, how many did they eat in one hour? _____

16. Mrs. Martin's family uses a gallon of milk a day. How many quarts of milk will they use in a week? _____

How many quarts will they use in a year? (52 weeks) _____

Divide, and then check by multiplying. Use estimation to help you if needed. Write any remainders as fractions.

1. 3 | 3 7 6 6

2. check for #1

3. 6 | 8 9 8 9

4. check for #3

5. 71 | 4 0 0

6. check for #5

7. 44 | 3 5 2

8. check for #7

Multiply.

9.

	3,	4	4	5
x			9	3

10.

	2,	3	1	7
x			6	4

11.

	8,	9	1	2
x			2	5

Fill in the blanks.

12. 5,280 ft = _____ Yd

13. 4 tons = _____ lb

14. 1,000 ft = _____ in

15. Chris walked two miles. How many yards did he walk? _____
Hint: Look at your answer for #12.

16. Laura was teaching her sister about parallel and perpendicular
lines. She drew an uppercase "T." What kind of line was she
illustrating? _____

Estimate each answer, and then divide and compare your answers.
Check your final answer by multiplying. The first two are done for you.

1. 72⟌7891 → (70) (8000)

2.

	1	0	9	43/72
72	7	8	9	1
-7	2	0	0
	6	9	1
	-6	4	8
		4	3

```
      72
   x 109
     648
   7200
   7848
  +  43
   7891
```

3. 19⟌3800 → ( ) ( )

4. 19⟌3 8 0 0

5. 55⟌6920 → ( ) ( )

6. 55⟌6 9 2 0

7. Mr. Rich has $6,929 in his wallet. If he earns $41 an hour, how long did it take him to earn that much? _____

8. A store owner gets $15 profit for each new coat he sells. How many coats must he sell to make $1,875? _____

24B

Estimate each answer, and then divide and compare your answers.
Check your final answer by multiplying. The first two are done for you.

1. $63 \overline{)4555}$ → (60) $\overline{)(5\ 0\ 0\ 0)}$ (80)

2.
```
        7 2 | 19/63      6 3
63 | 4 5 5 5             x 7 2
   -4 4 1 0             1 2 6
     1 4 5             4 4 1 0
    -1 2 6             4 5 3 6
         1 9           +   1 9
                        4 5 5 5
```

3. $91 \overline{)3863}$ → ( ) $\overline{)(\qquad)}$

4.
```
           4 2 | r. 41/91
91 | 3 8 6 3
   -3 6 4
      2 3
     -1 8 2
        4 1
```

5. $34 \overline{)5592}$ → ( ) $\overline{)(\qquad)}$

6.
```
          1 6 4 | r. 16/34      16/34
34 | 5 5 9 2                    x  6
   -3 4                         204
     2 1 9
    -2 0 4                        4
        1 5 2                     34
       -1 3 6                    x 4
           1 6                   136
```

7. A fisherman caught 4,275 fish. He divided the fish into boxes holding 45 fish each. How many boxes of fish does he have to sell? _____

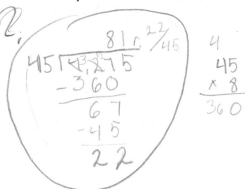

8. When Noah finished the ark, some animals boarded in groups of 14. If 1,008 animals were divided into groups of 14 each, how many groups were there? _____

24C

Estimate each answer, and then divide and compare your answers. Check your final answer by multiplying.

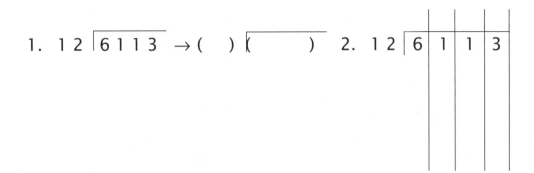

1. 12)‾6 1 1 3 → ( ) ‾( )   2. 12)‾6 | 1 | 1 | 3

3. 75)‾4 1 4 5 → ( ) ( )   4. 75)‾4 | 1 | 4 | 5

5. 46)‾7 0 0 3 → ( ) ( )   6. 46)‾7 | 0 | 0 | 3

7. Grace Joy earned $7,000 in 35 weeks. How much did she earn in one week?_____

8. A sports store owner added up all the balls he sold last year and got a total of 9,360. What was the average number of balls sold per week? (There are 52 weeks in a year.) _____

24D

Divide, and then check by multiplying. Use estimation to help you if needed. Write any remainders as fractions.

1. 25 $\overline{)5\,5\,5\,3}$

2. check for #1

3. 63 $\overline{)5\,9\,8\,5}$

4. check for #3

5. 8 $\overline{)2\,9\,1\,0}$

6. check for #5

7. 11 $\overline{)1\,0\,8}$

8. check for #7

Multiply upside down. The first one is done for you.

9.

		1	2	2
×	4	3	5	3
		3	6	6
	5	0	0	0
²3	6	6	0	0
¹4	8	8	0	0
5	3	1,	0	6	6

10.

	3	2	4
×	3	1	5	2

11.

	7	9	3
×	1	2	8	4

12. David's room is a rectangle that measures 12 feet by 14 feet. What is the area of his room? _____

13. Kate was trying to grow prize-winning tomatoes. She weighed the tomatoes from one plant and got the following weights: 16 ounces, 14 ounces, 7 ounces, 20 ounces, and 8 ounces. What was the average weight of the tomatoes? _____

Was the average weight more or less than a pound? _____

14. A basketball player is seven feet tall. How many inches tall is he?
_____

Divide, and then check by multiplying. Use estimation to help you if needed. Write any remainders as fractions.

1. 34 ⟌ 2 9 9 1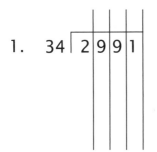

2. check for #1

3. 12 ⟌ 6 5 8 1

4. check for #3

5. 5 ⟌ 4 6 3 3

6. check for #5

7. 27 ⟌ 4 9 5

8. check for #7

Multiply upside down.

9.
$$\begin{array}{c|c|c|c}
 & 1 & 6 & 2 \\
\times\ 4 & 1 & 9 & 5
\end{array}$$

10.
$$\begin{array}{c|c|c|c}
 & 2 & 8 & 1 \\
\times\ 2 & 7 & 0 & 3
\end{array}$$

11.
$$\begin{array}{c|c|c|c}
 & 4 & 3 & 7 \\
\times\ 1 & 5 & 8 & 8
\end{array}$$

12. Stephanie measured a right triangle and found the base was 10 inches and the height was 16 inches. What was the area of the triangle? _____

13. Chucky has a 2,266-mile drive to make. He wants to drive the same distance every day. If he plans 11 days for the trip, how many miles must he drive each day? _____

14. Write a letter of the alphabet that has parallel lines in it. _____

24F

Divide, and then check by multiplying. Use estimation to help you
if needed. Write any remainders as fractions.

1. 14 | 1 | 6 | 1 | 3

2. check for #1

3. 91 | 1 | 2 | 2 | 3

4. check for #3

5. 4 | 7 | 5 | 6 | 2

6. check for #5

7. 13 | 2 | 9 | 4

8. check for #7

Multiply upside down. The first one is done for you.

9.

	5	6	1
×	1	3	6	1

10.

	9	4	6
×	3	7	2	2

11.

	8	3	7
×	4	6	8	3

12. Kimberly drew a trapezoid with bases of 5 in and 7 in and a height of 12 in. What is the area of the trapezoid? _____

13. Twenty people want to go on a field trip. If the vehicles hold eight passengers each, how many vehicles are needed? _____

   Should your remainder be written as a fraction? _____

14. Write a letter of the alphabet that has perpendicular lines in it.

   _____

25A

Estimate each answer, and then divide and compare your answers. Check your final answer by multiplying. The first two are done for you. (Lesson Practice 25B has problems with three digits into six digits.)

1. $32 \overline{)48{,}621} \rightarrow (30) \overline{)(50{,}000)}$ (1,000)

2.

$$
32 \overline{)48621} \quad 1519 \tfrac{13}{31}
$$

$$
\begin{array}{r}
-32000 \\ \hline
16621 \\
16000 \\ \hline
621 \\
320 \\ \hline
301 \\
288 \\ \hline
13
\end{array}
$$

$$
\begin{array}{r}
32 \\
\times 1519 \\ \hline
288 \\
320 \\
16000 \\
32000 \\ \hline
48608 \\
+13 \\ \hline
48{,}621
\end{array}
$$

3. $56 \overline{)59{,}038} \rightarrow (\quad\quad) \overline{)(\quad\quad\quad\quad)}$

4. $56 \overline{)59038}$

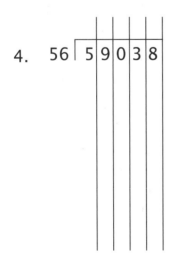

5. 73$\overline{)71{,}905}$ → (   )|(   )

6. 73$\overline{)7\,1\,9\,0\,5}$

7. Derek earns $20 a day mowing lawns. How many days must he work to earn $40,000? _____

Estimate each answer, and then divide and compare your answers. Check your final answer by multiplying. The first two are done for you.

$(2,0\ 0\ 0)$

1. $236\overline{\smash{\big)}\,3\ 8\ 7,1\ 4\ 5} \rightarrow (200)\overline{\smash{\big)}\,(4\ 0\ 0,0\ 0\ 0)}$

2.

```
                1 6 4 0 | 105
                        | ───
   236 | 3 8 7 1 4 5    | 236                    2 3 6
        -2 3 6 0 0 0                           × 1 6 4 0
         1 5 1 1 4 5                               9 4 0 0
         1 4 1 6 0 0                           1 4 1 6 0 0
             9 5 4 5                           2 3 6 0 0 0
             9 4 4 0                           3 8 7 0 4 0
               1 0 5                             + 1 0 5
                                              3 8 7,1 4 5
```

3. $503\overline{\smash{\big)}\,8\ 2\ 3,5\ 3\ 6} \rightarrow (\quad\quad)\overline{\smash{\big)}\,(\quad\quad\quad\quad\quad)}$

4. $503\overline{\smash{\big)}\,8\ 2\ 3\ 5\ 3\ 6}$

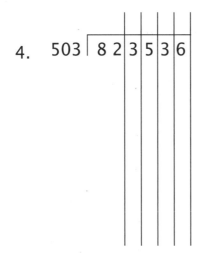

5. Alison kept track of her bike rides for a whole year and found that she had ridden 963,600 feet last year. There are 365 days in a year. Find Alison's average daily distance last year. _____

6. Jessica earns $26,052 a year. Since there are 52 weeks in a year, how much does Jessica earn each week? _____

Estimate each answer, and then divide and compare your answers.
Check your final answer by multiplying.

1. 35 $\overline{)7\,5{,}6\,2\,5}$ → (   )$\overline{()}$

2. 35 $\overline{)7\,|5\,|6\,|2\,|5}$

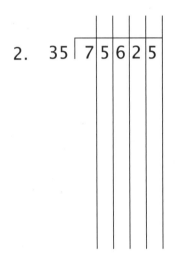

3. 858 $\overline{)9\,3\,1{,}4\,6\,3}$ → (   )$\overline{()}$

4. 858 $\overline{)9\,3\,|1\,|4\,|6\,|3}$

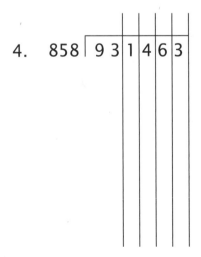

5. How many pounds are there in 12,560 ounces? _____

6. Only 300 people a day are allowed to tour the old house. If 900,000 people want to visit the house, how many days will it take? _____

25D

Divide, and then check by multiplying. Use estimation to help you if needed. Write any remainders as fractions.

1. 38 | 6 3 4 1 3

2. check for #1

3. 357 | 9 8 7 6 1 4

4. check for #3

5. 9 | 9 2 9 1

6. check for #5

7. 12 | 6 8 3 1

8. check for #7

Use what you know about area and your division skills to find the missing part of each parallelogram or rectangle. The drawings are sketches, and may not show the real lengths of the missing sides.

9. area = 525 sq in   base =

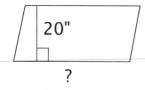

10. area = 28 sq ft   height =

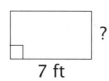

11. area = 500 sq in   height =

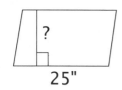

12. A plane flew at 500 miles an hour for 12 hours. How far did the plane fly? _____

13. Another plane covered 4,800 miles in 12 hours. How fast was that plane flying (miles per hour)? _____

14. Steve started his flight in the first plane (#12), and then got on the second plane (#13) to complete his trip. How many miles did he fly in all? _____

25E

Divide, and then check by multiplying. Use estimation to help you if needed. Write any remainders as fractions.

1. 63 ⟌ 6 8 9 8 2

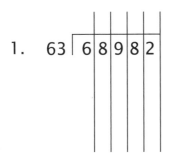

2. check for #1

3. 321 ⟌ 6 9 2 4 3 6

4. check for #3

5. 2 ⟌ 3 3 2 0

6. check for #5

7. 52 ⟌ 9 5 5 5

8. check for #7

Use what you know about area and your division skills to find the missing part of each parallelogram or rectangle.

9. area = 860 sq in   base = _____

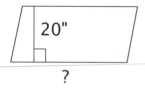
20"

?

10. area = 88 sq ft   height = _____

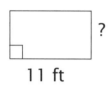
?

11 ft

11. area = 255 sq in   height = _____

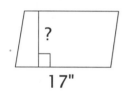
?

17"

12. Ray bought two cases of eggs for his store. If each case contained 360 eggs, how many dozen eggs did Ray buy? _____

13. The area of Rachel's room is 143 square feet. If her room is 11 feet wide, how long is it? _____

14. Gabe has saved $792 towards a computer that costs $1,843. How much does he still have to save? _____

Divide, and then check by multiplying. Use estimation to help you if needed. Write any remainders as fractions.

1. 31) 4 4 5 6 8

2. check for #1

3. 420) 2 5 2 0 0 0

4. check for #3

5. 8) 5 6 8 3

6. check for #5

7. 18) 1 5 9 6

8. check for #7

Use what you know about area and your division skills to find the missing part of each parallelogram or rectangle. The drawings are sketches.

9. area = 110 sq in   base = _____

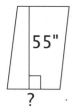

10. area = 10,560 sq ft   height = _____

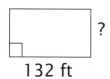

11. area = 868 sq in   height = _____

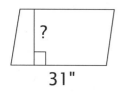

12. Rob's bicycle weighs 560 ounces. How many pounds does it weigh? _____

13. How many ounces are there in one ton? _____

14. In three days, Tim drove 543 miles, 324 miles, and 480 miles. What is his average number of miles per day? _____

Find the volume. The first one is done for you.

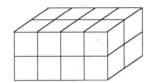

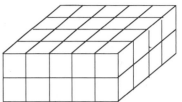

1. V = __16__ cubic units

2. V = __40__ cubic units

V = Bh
V = (4 × 2) × 2
V = 16 cubic units

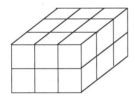

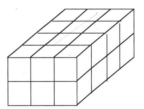

3. V = __18__ cubic units

4. V = __24__ cubic units

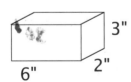

3"
6"   2"

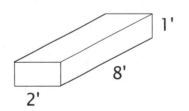

1'
8'
2'

5. V = __36__ cubic inches

6. V = __16__ cubic feet

7.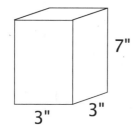

8.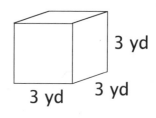

V = _6̲3̲_ cubic inches   V = _2̲7̲_ cubic yards

9. Eric's birthday cake is 10 inches wide, 12 inches long, and 4 inches high. How many cubic inches of cake does he have? _4̲8̲0̲_"

10. A cupboard is two feet wide, three feet deep, and five feet high. How many cubic feet of groceries can be stored in it? _3̲0̲_'

DELTA

Find the volume.

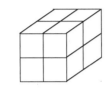

1. V = ___8___ cubic units

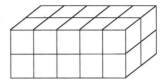

2. V = ___20___ cubic units

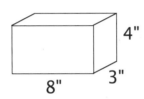

3. V = ___96___ cubic inches

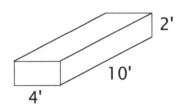

4. V = ___80___ cubic feet

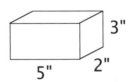

5. V = ___30___ cubic inches

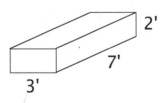

6. V = ___42___ cubic feet

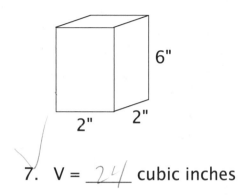

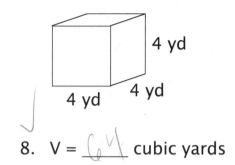

7. V = _24_ cubic inches

8. V = _64_ cubic yards

9. A room measures four yards by three yards. The ceiling is three yards high. What is the volume of the air in the room? _36_

10. Jim wants to build a pile of blocks five long, six wide, and three high. How many blocks does he need? _90_

26C

Find the volume.

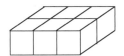

1. V = _____ cubic units

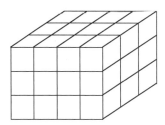

2. V = _____ cubic units

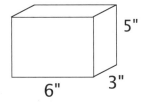

3. V = _____ cu in

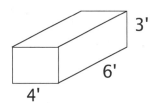

4. V = _____ cu ft

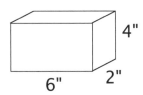

5. V = _____ cu in

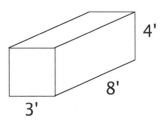

6. V = _____ cu ft

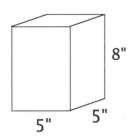

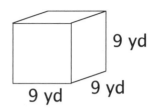

7. V = _____ cu in

8. V = _____ cu yd

9. One cubic foot holds about seven gallons of water. How many gallons will fit in four cubic feet? _____

10. About how many gallons of water would fit in a bathtub that is five feet by two feet by one foot? _____

Find the volume.

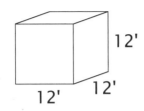

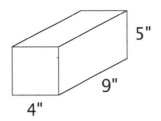

1. V = _____ cu ft

2. V = _____ cu in

Divide, and then check by multiplying. Use estimation to help you if needed.

3. 5 ⟌ 6 5 3 2

4. check for #3

5. 36 ⟌ 8 8 5 6 4

6. check for #5

Fill in the blanks.

7. 10,560 ft = _____ yd   8. 100 yd = _____ ft

9. 300 ft = _____ in

10. Seven gallons of water fill up one cubic foot of space. How many cubic feet will 35 gallons fill? _____

11. A swimming pool has 84 cubic feet of space. How many gallons of water will it take to fill it to the brim? _____

12. Which holds more, a 10 in by 4 in by 5 in pan, or a 10 in by 6 in by 3 in pan? _____

13. Riley has 32 quarters. How many dollars could she get in exchange for her quarters? _____

14. It is 576 miles to Westchester. If Drew bikes 24 miles a day, how many days will it take him to get there? _____

15. How many ounces are there in a 10-pound bag of flour? _____

Find the volume.

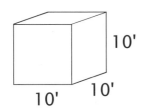

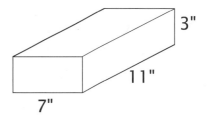

1. V = _____ cu ft

2. V = _____ cu in

Divide, and then check by multiplying. Use estimation to help you if needed.

3. 18 | 2 | 8 | 8

4. check for #3

5. 248 | 2 | 9 | 8 | 3 | 4 | 1

6. check for #5

Fill in the blanks.

7. 8 tons = _____ lb

8. 400 oz = _____ lb

9. 60 lb = _____ oz

10. George dug a hole seven feet long, six feet wide, and two feet deep. At seven gallons to a cubic foot, how many gallons of water would it take to fill his hole? _____

11. Isaac caught 324 fireflies. If he divided them evenly among his three brothers and himself, how many fireflies did each boy receive? _____

12. Joe gained 15 pounds and Jim gained 179 ounces. Who gained the most weight? _____

13. A business sold $549,600 worth of toys last year. On average, what was the monthly value of the toys it sold? _____

14. In December, the store actually sold $65,600 worth of toys. How much more was that than the monthly average? (See the answer to #13.) _____

15. A triangle has a base of 10 inches and a height of 8 inches. What is the area of the triangle? _____

Find the volume.

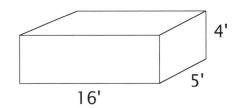

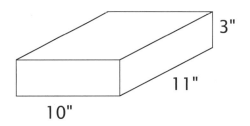

1. V = _____ cu ft

2. V = _____ cu in

Divide, and then check by multiplying. Use estimation to help you if needed.

3. 6 | 1 6 2 6 0

4. check for #3

5. 13 | 9 3 3 5 1

6. check for #5

Fill in the blanks.

7. 18 pt = _____ qt

8. 75 dollars = _____ quarters

9. 64 gal = _____ qt

10. A biologist placed 25,000 fish eggs in tanks to hatch. If he has five tanks and put the same number of eggs in each, how many eggs are in each tank? _____

11. One fish tank (#10) measures 10 feet by 10 feet and can be filled to a depth of five feet. What is the volume of water in each tank? _____

12. How many gallons of water will it take to fill one of the tanks described in #11? _____

13. A gallon of water weighs about eight pounds. What is the weight of the water in one fish tank? (#12) _____

14. Are the opposite sides of a rectangle parallel? _____

15. A trapezoid has bases of 14 inches and 8 inches and a height of 10 inches. What is the area of the trapezoid? _____

Do each problem with the blocks. Fill in the blanks below the pictures, and then write the problem and the answer to the right. The first one is done for you.

1. Select __10__ blocks.

__5__ equal parts.

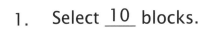

Count __2__ of those parts.

$\frac{2}{5}$ of __10__ is __4__

2. Select __6__ blocks.

Divide into __2__ equal parts.

Count __1__ of those parts.

$\frac{1}{2}$ of __6__ is __3__

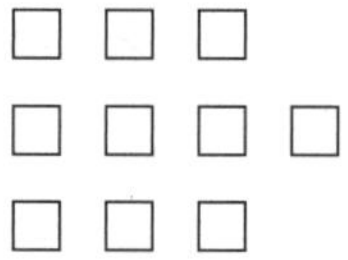

3. Select ___ blocks.

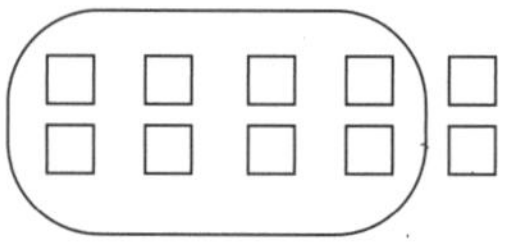

Count ___ of those parts.

Divide into ___ equal parts.

—— of __ is __

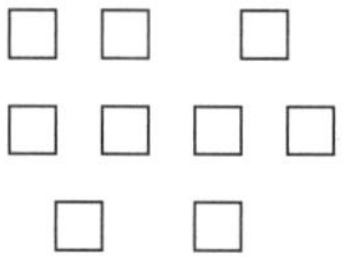

4. Select ___ blocks.

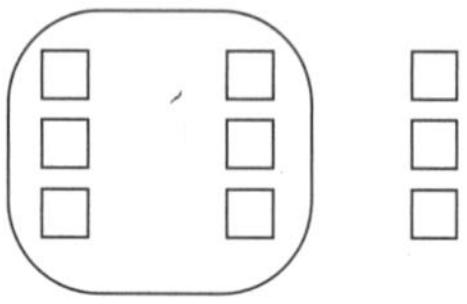

Count ___ of those parts.

Divide into ___ equal parts.

—— of __ is __

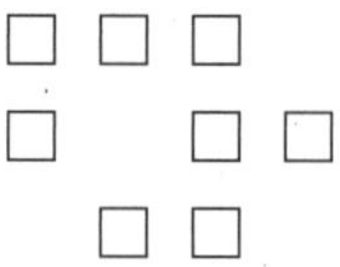

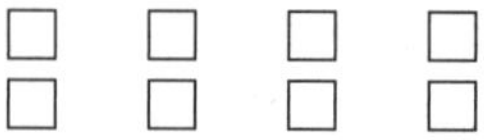

5. Select ___ blocks.

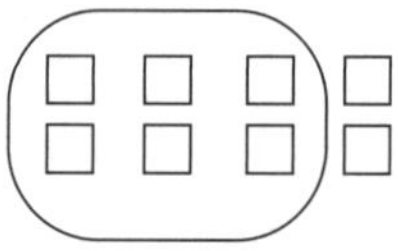

Count ___ of those parts.

Divide into ___ equal parts.

—— of __ is __

Build the problem, and then write the correct solution. The first one is done for you.

1. Select 20 blocks.

    Divide them into five equal parts.

    Count two of the parts. $\frac{2}{5}$ of _20_ is _8_

2. Select 18 blocks.

    Divide them into two equal parts.

    Count one of the parts. $\frac{1}{2}$ of _18_ is _9_

3. Select 12 blocks.

    Divide them into six equal parts.

    Count five of the parts. $\frac{5}{6}$ of _12_ is _10_

Read the problem, build it, and write the answer in the blank.

4. Three-fifths of twenty is _12_ .

5. Two-thirds of six is _4_ .

6. One-half of eight is _4_ .

Solve.

7. $\frac{1}{3}$ of 6 = _2_

8. $\frac{1}{4}$ of 8 = _2_

9. $\frac{4}{5}$ of 10 = _8_

10. $\frac{1}{2}$ of 6 = _3_

11. $\frac{2}{3}$ of 12 = _8_

12. $\frac{1}{2}$ of 8 = _4_

13. It was warm enough where Devan lived to swim 1/4 of the year. How many months could Devan swim? _3_

14. Jacob decided that he needed new gloves because 1/2 of the fingers in his old ones had holes. How many fingers have holes? _5_

15. Isabella was disappointed because 2/5 of the daffodil bulbs she planted did not come up. If she planted 10 bulbs, how many did not come up? _4_

Build the problem, and then write the correct solution.

1. Select nine blocks.

   Divide them into three equal parts.

   Count one of the parts. $\dfrac{1}{3}$ of _9_ is _3_

2. Select 10 blocks.

   Divide them into five equal parts.

   Count three of the parts. $\dfrac{3}{5}$ of _10_ is _6_

3. Select 12 blocks.

   Divide them into four equal parts.

   Count two of the parts. $\dfrac{2}{4}$ of _12_ is _4_

Read the problem, build it, and write the answer in the blank.

4. Two-fourths of sixteen is _8_ .

5. One-fifth of ten is _2_ .

6. Five-sixths of eighteen is _15_ .

Solve.

7. $\frac{3}{4}$ of 12 = _9_

8. $\frac{3}{5}$ of 10 = _6_

9. $\frac{1}{2}$ of 4 = _2_

10. $\frac{1}{3}$ of 12 = _4_

11. $\frac{1}{2}$ of 12 = _6_

12. $\frac{7}{8}$ of 16 = _13_

13. Micah bought 14 roses. If he gave 2/7 of them to his mother for Mother's Day, how many roses did she receive? _4_

14. Kaylee has 20 fingers and toes. If she has bandages on 1/5 of them, how many bandages is she wearing? _4_

15. Anah is 16 years old. If she lived in Ohio for 3/4 of those years, how many years did she live in Ohio? _12_

Solve.

1. $\dfrac{1}{2}$ of 6 = ____

2. $\dfrac{3}{4}$ of 16 = ____

3. $\dfrac{2}{5}$ of 20 = ____

Find the volume.

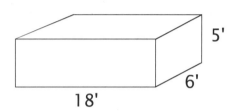

4. V = ____ cubic feet

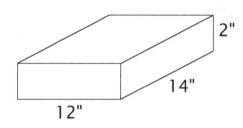

5. V = ____ cubic inches

Divide, and then check by multiplying. Use estimation to help you if needed.

6. 4) 2 4 0 1 5

7. check for #6

8. 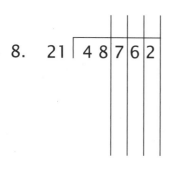 21 | 4 8 7 6 2

9. check for #8

Fill in the blanks.

10. 2 miles = _____ ft

11. 4 tons = _____ lb

12. 75 ft = _____ in

13. Eighteen girls came to the party. One-third of them wore blue dresses. How many of the girls wore blue dresses? _____

14. How many gallons of water are needed to fill a tank that measures 3 ft by 3 ft by 4 ft? _____

15. At eight pounds per gallon, what is the weight of the water in the tank in #14? _____

Solve.

1. $\frac{1}{6}$ of 12 = _____

2. $\frac{4}{7}$ of 21 = _____

3. $\frac{1}{8}$ of 16 = _____

Find the volume.

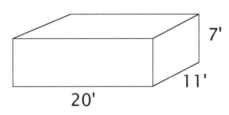

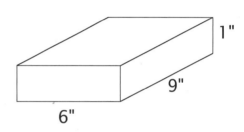

4. V = _____ cu ft

5. V = _____ cu in

Divide, and then check by multiplying. Use estimation to help you if needed.

6. 9) 2 9 5 0 2

7. check for #6

8. 44 | 8 9 3 6 7

9. check for #8

Fill in the blanks.

10. 5 yd = _____ ft

11. 7 qt = _____ pt

12. 20 gal = _____ qt

13. Nine boys got together to play ball. Three-ninths of them brought their own bats. How many brought their own bats?
    _____

14. Raleigh rides his bike 1/6 of the day. Since there are 24 hours in a day, how many hours a day does he ride his bike? _____

15. There are 60 minutes in an hour. Find how many minutes a day Raleigh rides his bike. (#14) _____

Solve.

1. $\frac{3}{4}$ of 20 = _____

2. $\frac{1}{3}$ of 12 = _____

3. $\frac{1}{2}$ of 14 = _____

Find the volume.

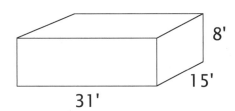

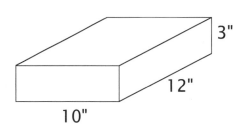

4. V = _____ cu ft

5. V = _____ cu in

Divide, and then check by multiplying. Use estimation to help you if needed.

6. 6 | 1 8 0 3 6

7. check for #6

8. 25 $\overline{)3\ 5\ 4\ 2\ 5}$

9. check for #8

Fill in the blanks.

10. 20 lb = _____ oz

11. 35 dollars = _____ quarters

12. 3 mi = _____ ft

Challengers: You can do these if you are careful.

13. Joshua is interested in the population of India. There are 8,227,332 people in Bombay; 3,305,006 people in Calcutta; and 4,884,234 people in Delhi. What is the total population of the three cities? _____

14. Steven found that the population of New York City is 8,274,961 and the population of Los Angeles is 7,477,503. What is the difference between the populations of the two cities? _____

15. Andrew says that if you add the populations of New York City and Los Angeles, you have about the same number of people as Mexico City (14,445,000). What is the difference between the total population of New York and Los Angeles, and the population of Mexico City? _____

Write the number represented by the Roman numerals.
The first one is done for you.

1. VIII = __8__

2. XXIII = ___

3. XVII = ___

4. L = ___

5. CC = ___

6. XC = ___

7. LXX = ___

8. XLVI = ___

Use Roman numerals to represent the number. The first one is done for you.

9. 35 = __XXXV__

10. 14 = _____

11. 31 = _____

12. 48 = ___

13. 150 = ___

14. 325 = ___

15. 249 = ___

16. 63 = ___

17. What time is it?_____

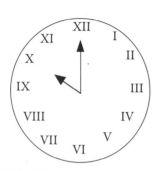

18. Trevor's outline has 14 points. What Roman numeral should he use for the last point? _____

19. Which three symbols may be used three times in a row? _____

20. Which two symbols may be used only once in a row? _____

Write the number represented by the Roman numerals.

1. IX = ____

2. XXXVI = ____

3. CXXIV = ____

4. CLII = ____

5. XCVIII = ____

6. CXCII = ____

7. CXLV = ____

8. CCCXV = ____

Use Roman numerals to represent the number.

9. 18 = ____

10. 26 = ____

11. 94 = ____

12. 43 = ____

13. 258 = ____

14. 317 = ____

15. 262 = ____

16. 189 = ____

17. What time is it? _____

18. If I and X are to the left of a larger symbol, do we add or subtract their value? _____

19. Will you ever find LLL used in Roman numerals? _____

20. Brandon is writing an outline. What Roman numeral should he use for the sixth point? _____

Write the number represented by the Roman numerals.

1. XIX = ____

2. XLIX = ____

3. XCIV = ____

4. LIII = ____

5. CXLVII = ____

6. XVIII = ____

7. XXXIX = ____

8. CCXXII = ____

Use Roman numerals to represent the number.

9. 94 = ____

10. 13 = ____

11. 28 = ____

12. 45 = ____

13. 359 = ____

14. 108 = ____

15. 311 = ____

16. 274 = ____

17. What time is it? _____

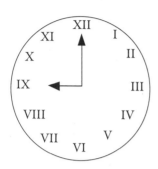

18. The last point in Sarah's outline is XX. How many points does she have in her outline? _____

19. The shadow on the sundial pointed to VI. What time was it? _____

20. How many times in a row may you use the symbol C? _____

Write the number represented by the Roman numerals.

1. VIII = ___

2. XXIV = ___

3. CXL = ___

4. XLII = ___

Use Roman numerals to represent the number.

5. 61 = ___

6. 48 = ___

7. 152 = ___

8. 210 = ___

Solve.

9. $\frac{1}{3}$ of 12 = ___

10. $\frac{2}{7}$ of 21 = ___

11. $\frac{4}{5}$ of 10 = ___

Find the area.

12. A = _____

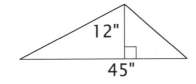

Divide, and then check by multiplying. Use estimation to help you if needed.

13. 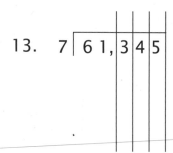 7 | 6 1,3 4 5

14. check for #13

15. 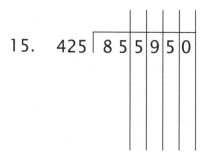 425 | 8 5 5 9 5 0

16. check for #15

17. There are 24 students in the class. One-third of them have blue eyes. How many of the children have blue eyes? _____

18. Brigette read seven books the first week, nine the second, eleven the third, and one the fourth week. What was the average number of books she read each week? _____

Write the number represented by the Roman numerals.

1. XXIV = ____

2. CCLXXI = ____

3. CXLV = ____

4. XVIII = ____

Use Roman numerals to represent the number.

5. 75 = ____

6. 92 = ____

7. 380 = ____

8. 111 = ____

Solve.

9. $\frac{1}{4}$ of 16 = ____

10. $\frac{5}{6}$ of 18 = ____

11. $\frac{1}{2}$ of 20 = ____

Find the area.

12.

A = _____

Divide, and then check by multiplying. Use estimation to help you if needed.

13. 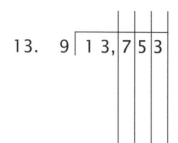 9 | 1 3, 7 5 3

14. check for #13

15. 350 | 7 8 4 5 9 6

16. check for #15

17. The following amounts of rain fell the last four months:
March–12", April–11", May-2", and June-3".

What is the average rainfall for the last four months? _____

18. Angela is five feet and seven inches tall. Give her height in inches. _____

Write the number represented by the Roman numerals.

1. CXL = ____

2. CCCLIV = ____

3. XXVII = ____

4. LXXXI = ____

Use Roman numerals to represent the number.

5. 34 = ____

6. 56 = ____

7. 299 = ____

8. 355 = ____

Solve.

9. $\frac{2}{3}$ of 9 = ____

10. $\frac{3}{5}$ of 15 = ____

11. $\frac{1}{4}$ of 12 = ____

Find the area.

12.

65 mi

65 mi

A = _____

Divide, and then check by multiplying. Use estimation to help you if needed.

13. 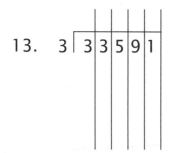 3 | 3 3 5 9 1

14. check for #13

15. 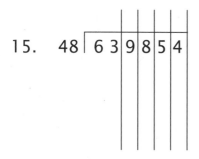 48 | 6 3 9 8 5 4

16. check for #15

17. Are railroad tracks parallel or perpendicular to each other? _____

18. Holly likes Georgia because it is sunny 3/4 of the year. How many months are sunny in Georgia? _____

Find the denominators and numerators of the rectangles. The first one is done for you.

1. $\dfrac{\text{numerator}}{\text{denominator}} = \dfrac{2}{6}$

2. $\dfrac{\text{numerator}}{\text{denominator}} = \underline{\quad}$

3. $\dfrac{\text{numerator}}{\text{denominator}} = \underline{\quad}$

4. $\dfrac{\text{numerator}}{\text{denominator}} = \underline{\quad}$

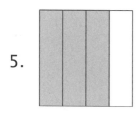

5. $\dfrac{\text{numerator}}{\text{denominator}} = \underline{}$

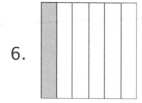

6. $\dfrac{\text{numerator}}{\text{denominator}} = \underline{}$

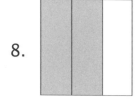

7. $\dfrac{\text{numerator}}{\text{denominator}} = \underline{}$

8. $\dfrac{\text{numerator}}{\text{denominator}} = \underline{}$

9. Mom wants to give everyone 1/6 of a pie. Into how many pieces should she cut the pie? _____

Shade the rectangles to show the given fractions.
The first one is done for you.

1. 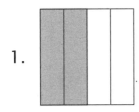 $\dfrac{\text{numerator}}{\text{denominator}} = \dfrac{2}{4}$

2. $\dfrac{\text{numerator}}{\text{denominator}} = \dfrac{3}{6}$

3. $\dfrac{\text{numerator}}{\text{denominator}} = \dfrac{1}{5}$

4. $\dfrac{\text{numerator}}{\text{denominator}} = \dfrac{1}{3}$

5.  $\dfrac{\text{numerator}}{\text{denominator}} = \dfrac{5}{6}$

6.  $\dfrac{\text{numerator}}{\text{denominator}} = \dfrac{1}{4}$

7. $\dfrac{\text{numerator}}{\text{denominator}} = \dfrac{3}{5}$

8. $\dfrac{\text{numerator}}{\text{denominator}} = \dfrac{2}{2}$

9. A cake is cut into 10 pieces. If Tim gets 1/10 of the cake, how many pieces will he get? _____

Draw lines and shade the right number of rectangles to represent each fraction. The first one is done for you.

1. 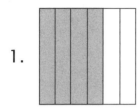 $\dfrac{\text{numerator}}{\text{denominator}} = \dfrac{4}{6}$

2. $\dfrac{\text{numerator}}{\text{denominator}} = \dfrac{4}{4}$

3. $\dfrac{\text{numerator}}{\text{denominator}} = \dfrac{2}{3}$

4. $\dfrac{\text{numerator}}{\text{denominator}} = \dfrac{4}{5}$

5. $\dfrac{\text{numerator}}{\text{denominator}} = \dfrac{3}{4}$

6. $\dfrac{\text{numerator}}{\text{denominator}} = \dfrac{2}{6}$

7. $\dfrac{\text{numerator}}{\text{denominator}} = \dfrac{1}{2}$

8. $\dfrac{\text{numerator}}{\text{denominator}} = \dfrac{3}{5}$

9. A pizza is cut into eight pieces. If Sharon gets 3/8 of the pizza, how many pieces will she get? _____

29D

Find the denominators and numerators of the rectangles.

1. $\dfrac{\text{numerator}}{\text{denominator}} = \underline{\quad}$

2. $\dfrac{\text{numerator}}{\text{denominator}} = \underline{\quad}$

Write the number represented by the Roman numerals.

3. IX = ____

4. XVII = ____

5. CCL = ____

6. XCIX = ____

Use Roman numerals to represent the number.

7. 91 = ____

8. 54 = ____

9. 63 = ____

10. 391 = ____

Find the area.

11. A = _____

12. A = _____

32"
12"

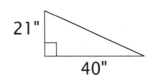

21"
40"

Divide, and then check by multiplying. Use estimation to help you if needed.

13. 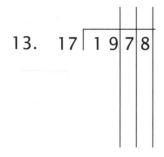 17 | 1 9 | 7 | 8 |

14. check for #13

15. 38 | 4 0 | 3 | 1 | 8 |

16. check for #15

17. Two roads meet and intersect at right angles in the middle of town. Are they parallel or perpendicular? _____

18. Andrea counted out 15 jelly beans. One-third of them were red. How many jelly beans were red? _____

Shade the rectangles to show the given fractions.

1. $\dfrac{\text{numerator}}{\text{denominator}} = \dfrac{3}{3}$

2. $\dfrac{\text{numerator}}{\text{denominator}} = \dfrac{2}{5}$

Write the number represented by the Roman numerals.

3. LXXII = ____

4. XXXIV = ____

5. CXCIV = ____

6. LXV = ____

Use Roman numerals to represent the number.

7. 25 = ____

8. 13 = ____

9. 48 = ____

10. 160 = ____

Find the volume.

11. V = _____

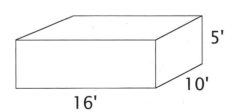

12. V = _____

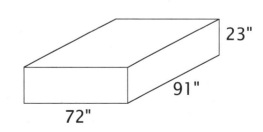

Divide, and then check by multiplying. Use estimation to help you if needed.

13. 65 | 3 4 5 9 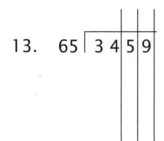   14. check for #13

15. 21 | 5 5 6 2 7   16. check for #15

17. Dan drove 200 miles to visit his parents. If his average speed was 50 miles an hour, how long did the trip take him? (200 ÷ 50) _____

18. Ruth had 12 cookies. If she gave 3/4 of them to Naomi, how many cookies did Naomi get? _____

How many cookies did Ruth have left? _____

Draw lines and shade the right number of rectangles to represent each fraction.

1. ☐ $\dfrac{\text{numerator}}{\text{denominator}} = \dfrac{1}{2}$

2. ☐ $\dfrac{\text{numerator}}{\text{denominator}} = \dfrac{4}{5}$

Write the number represented by the Roman numerals.

3. XIV = ____   4. LXXXVI = ____

5. CCIX = ____   6. CXCVIII = ____

Use Roman numerals to represent the number.

7. 36 = ____   8. 14 = ____

9. 59 = ____   10. 273 = ____

Find the volume.

11. V = _____   12. V = _____

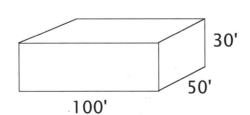

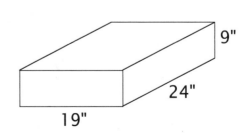

Divide, and then check by multiplying. Use estimation to help you if needed.

13. 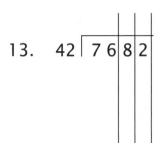 42 | 7 6 8 2

14. check for #13

15. 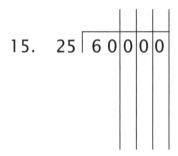 25 | 6 0 0 0 0

16. check for #15

17. Nate drove 350 miles to visit his brother. If his average speed was 60 miles an hour, how many hours did he drive? _____

18. Fifty people listened to the speech. One-half of them disagreed with the speaker. How many people disagreed? _____

30A

Write the number represented by the Roman numerals.
The first two are done for you.

1. MDCL = <u>1,650</u>

    1000 + 500 + 100 +

    50 = 1650

2. $\overline{\text{LIV}}$ = <u>54,000</u>

    50 + 4 = 54

    54 x 1,000 = 54,000

3. CD = _____

4. MCCL = _____

5. $\overline{\text{XLV}}$ = _____

6. CMLII = _____

7. DCC = _____

8. MMIII = _____

Use Roman numerals to represent the number. The first two are done for you.

9. 1525 = <u>MDXXV</u>

    1,000 + 500 +

    20 + 5 = MDXXV

10. 2,000,000 = <u>$\overline{\text{MM}}$</u>

    2,000 = MM

    2,000 x 1,000 = $\overline{\text{MM}}$

11. 578 = _____   12. 5,000 = _____

13. 2,146 = _____   14. 1,872 = _____

15. 10,000 = _____   16. 2,065 = _____

17. The front of Rachel's book says it was published in MCMXLV.
     What year was the book published? _____

18. How would you write the date in Roman numerals for a book that
     was published 10 years after the book in #17? _____

19. The American Declaration of Independence was signed in 1776.
     Write that date with Roman numerals. _____

20. A Roman general commanded 5,000 soldiers. How would he
     have recorded that with Roman numerals? _____

30B

Write the number represented by the Roman numerals.

1. DLVI = _____

2. MCDXXI = _____

3. DXLIX = _____

4. $\overline{V}$CC = _____

5. CMXXXI = _____

6. DXIV = _____

7. $\overline{MM}$ = _____

8. MCCCXX = _____

Use Roman numerals to represent the number.

9. 501 = _____

10. 625 = _____

11. 100,000 = _____   12. 3,000 = _____

13. 900,000 = _____   14. 432 = _____

15. 1,263 = _____   16. 1,967 = _____

17. If a book has the number MDCCCLXI on the title page, what year was it published? _____

18. A Roman farmer recorded a harvest of 563 sacks of grain. What did the number look like? _____

19. Columbus sailed in 1492. Write the date using Roman numerals.

_____

20. While studying a copy of an old Roman document, Abe saw a reference to MDLV people. How many people was that? _____

Write the number represented by the Roman numerals.

1. DLXXXIV = _____

2. DCVI = _____

3. CMXLV = _____

4. $\overline{XX}$ = _____

5. MCXL = _____

6. DCCCXXIX = _____

7. $\overline{L}$ = _____

8. $\overline{CM}$ = _____

Use Roman numerals to represent the number.

9. 582 = _____

10. 973 = _____

11. 1,053 = _____

12. 3,200 = _____

13. 444 = _____

14. 1,510 = _____

15. 3,995 = _____

16. 5,000 = _____

17. If a book has the number MDCCXCIX on the title page, in what year was it published? _____

18. Robin was born in 1966.
Write her birth date in Roman numerals. _____

19. A Roman soldier marched 459 leagues during his last campaign. How might he have recorded that number? _____

20. A monument refers to the date MLXVI. To what year is it referring? _____

Write the number represented by the Roman numerals.

1. MMCM = _____

2. DXXXIV = _____

3. MDC = _____

4. CMLV = _____

Use Roman numerals to represent the number.

5. 57 = _____

6. 109 = _____

7. 580 = _____

8. 1,411 = _____

Find the denominators and numerators of the rectangles.

9. $\dfrac{\text{numerator}}{\text{denominator}} = $ _____

10. $\dfrac{\text{numerator}}{\text{denominator}} = $ _____

Divide, and then check by multiplying. Use estimation to help you if needed.

11. 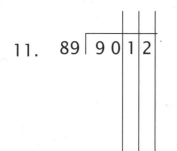 89 ⟌ 9 0 1 2

12. check for #11

13. 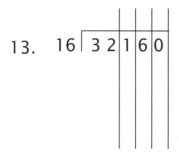 16 ⟌ 3 2 1 6 0

14. check for #13

15. Are the two parts of an uppercase "T" parallel or perpendicular? _____

16. A triangle has a base of 8 ft and a height of 9 ft. Its area is _____.

17. Penny earned the following scores on math tests: 85, 92, 73, and 98. What was her average score for math? _____

18. Brad earned $345, and then spent $128 on Christmas gifts for Aiden. How much money did he have left? _____

Write the number represented by the Roman numerals.

1. CMXXVIII = _____

2. CDXIV = _____

3. $\overline{\text{M}}$ = _____

4. LXXX = _____

Use Roman numerals to represent the number.

5. 29 = _____

6. 299 = _____

7. 2,999 = _____

8. 5,000 = _____

Find the denominators and numerators of the rectangles.

9. $\dfrac{\text{numerator}}{\text{denominator}}$ = ____

10. $\dfrac{\text{numerator}}{\text{denominator}}$ = ____

Divide, and then check by multiplying. Use estimation to help you if needed.

11. 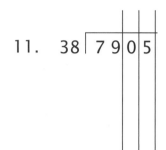 38 | 7 9 0 5

12. check for #11

13. 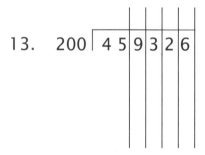 200 | 4 5 9 3 2 6

14. check for #13

15. How many quarts are there in 17 gallons? _____

16. Claire has $5 worth of quarters in her purse. How many quarters does she have? _____

17. A rectangular room measures 15 feet by 21 feet. How many square feet of carpet are needed to cover the floor? _____

18. Kerri bought 32 ounces of fruit. Divide to find how many pounds of fruit she has. _____

Write the number represented by the Roman numerals.

1. MMCCCX = _____

2. DXC = _____

3. $\bar{L}$ = _____

4. CLXXI = _____

Use Roman numerals to represent the number.

5. 17 = _____

6. 450 = _____

7. 3,269 = _____

8. 672 = _____

Divide, and then check by multiplying. Use estimation to help you if needed.

9. 51 | 6 8 0 3 2

10. 182 | 5 7 2 1 0 9

11. If an elephant weighs four tons, how many pounds does it weigh?_____

12. A trapezoid has bases of 6 ft and 8 ft and a height of 5 ft. What is the area of the trapezoid? _____

13. Twenty-four birds flew overhead. Two-thirds of them were swallows. How many swallows flew overhead? _____

14. Ben walked two miles. How many feet did he walk? _____

15. Round 3,499 to the nearest thousand. _____

16. My rectangular living room is five yards wide. How many feet wide is it? _____

    How many inches wide is the room? _____

17. At an average speed of 45 miles an hour, how long would it take to travel 315 miles? _____

18. What is the volume of a rectangular box that measures 5 ft by 6 ft by 3 ft? _____

Symbols & Tables

MONEY

1 nickel = 5 cents (5¢)

1 dime = 10 cents (10¢)

1 quarter = 25 cents (25¢)

1 dollar = 100 cents (100¢ or $1.00)

1 dollar = 4 quarters

MEASUREMENT

3 teaspoons (tsp) = 1 tablespoon (Tbsp)

2 pints (pt) = 1 quart (qt)

8 pints = 1 gallon (gal)

4 quarts = 1 gallon

12 inches (in) = 1 foot (ft)

3 feet = 1 yard (yd)

5,280 feet = 1 mile (mi)

16 ounces (oz) = 1 pound (lb)

2,000 pounds = 1 ton

60 seconds = 1 minute

60 minutes = 1 hour

7 days = 1 week

365 days = 1 year

52 weeks = 1 year

12 months = 1 year

1 dozen = 12

1 cubic foot of water is about 7 gallons

1 gallon of water weighs about 8 pounds

PLACE-VALUE NOTATION

31,452 = 30,000 + 1,000 + 400 + 50 + 2

EXPANDED NOTATION

1,452 = 1 x 1,000 + 4 x 100 + 5 x 10 + 2 x 1

SYMBOLS

=	equals
≈	approximately equal to
+	plus
−	minus
x	times
•	times
( )( )	times
¢	cents
$	dollars
'	foot
"	inch
<	less than
>	greater than
||	parallel
∟	right angle
⊥	perpendicular

4 ÷ 2   4 divided by 2

2)‾4   4 divided by 2

$\frac{4}{2}$ 4 divided by 2

AREA AND VOLUME

rectangle $A = bh$ (base times height)

parallelogram $A = bh$

triangle $A = \dfrac{bh}{2}$

trapezoid $A = \dfrac{b_1 + b_2}{2} \times h$

rectangular solid $V = Bh$

                     (area of base times height)

LABELS FOR PARTS OF PROBLEMS

Addition

```
  25    addend
 +16    addend
 ───
  41    sum
```

Multiplication

```
  33    multiplicand
×  5    multiplier
 ───
 165    product
```

Subtraction

```
  45    minuend
− 22    subtrahand
 ───
  23    difference
```

Division

```
          2   quotient
divisor 2│ 4   dividend
```

Glossary

A

Area - the number of square units in a rectangle or other two-dimensional figure

Average - the result of adding a series of numbers and dividing by the number of items in the series

Base - the top or bottom side of a shape

B-C

Borrowing - see Regrouping

Carrying - see Regrouping

Commutative property - the order of factors in a multiplication problem may be changed without changing the product. The commutative property also applies to addition.

Cube - a three-dimensional figure with each side the same length

Cubic units - the result of multiplying three dimensions. Answers to volume problems are in cubic units.

D

Denominator - the bottom number in a fraction. It tells how many total parts there are in the whole.

Dimension - the length of one of the sides of a rectangle or other shape

Dividend - the number being divided in a division problem

Divisor - the number that is being divided by in a division problem

E

Equation - a number sentence in which the value of one side is equal to the value of the other side

Estimation - used to get an approximate value of an answer

Even number - a number that ends in 0, 2, 4, 6, or 8. Even numbers are multiples of two.

Expanded notation - a way of writing numbers in which each amount is multiplied by its place value

F-G

Factors - the two sides of a rectangle, or the numbers multiplied in a multiplication problem

Fraction - one number written over another to show part of a whole. A fraction can also indicate division.

H-O

Height - the length of a line from the top to the bottom of a shape. It forms a right angle with the base.

Numerator - the top number in a fraction. It tells how many of the parts of a whole have been chosen.

P

Partial product - the result of multiplying by one digit of a multiple-digit problem

Parallel lines - two straight lines in the same plane that never cross or touch

Parallelogram - a shape with two pairs of parallel lines. A rectangle is a special kind of parallelogram.

Perpendicular lines - two straight lines that form a right angle where they meet

Place value - the position of a number that tells what value it is assigned

Place–value notation - a way of writing numbers to emphasize the place value of each part

Plane - a flat surface

Product - the answer to a multiplication problem

Q-R

Quadrilateral - a four-sided figure

Quotient - the answer to a division problem

Rectangle - a shape with four "square corners" or right angles

Rectangular solid - a three-dimensional shape with each side or face shaped like a rectangle

Regrouping - moving numbers from one place value to another in order to solve a problem. Also called "carrying" in addition and multiplication and "borrowing" in subtraction.

Right angle - a square corner (90° angle)

Roman numerals - a numbering system employed by the Roman Empire. It uses letters to represent the numbers

Rounding - writing a number as its closest ten, hundred, etc. in order to estimate

S-T

Square - a rectangle with all four sides the same length

Square units - the result of multiplying two dimensions. Answers to area problems are in square units.

Trapezoid - a four-sided shape or figure with two parallel sides

Triangle - a shape with three sides

U-V

Units - the first place value in the decimal system—also, starting from the right, the first three digits in a large number. The word units can also name measurements. Inches and feet are units of measure.

Volume - the number of cubic units in a three-dimensional shape

1044-0112

CONGRATULATIONS!!

To_____

On this_____ day of _____, 20___

You have just finished

Delta

You are becoming a math whiz!

Have fun doing the next book, which is

Epsilon

Psssst. Don't forget to thank your Teacher!

_____
Parent signature